6,50
NET

VIRGINIA
HISTORICAL SOCIETY DOCUMENTS

Volume 6

THE REVEREND JOHN CLAYTON
A Parson with a Scientific Mind

His Scientific Writings
and Other Related Papers

THE REVEREND JOHN CLAYTON

A Parson with a Scientific Mind

His Scientific Writings and Other Related Papers

Edited, with a Short Biographical Sketch, by

EDMUND BERKELEY
DOROTHY SMITH BERKELEY

Published for

THE VIRGINIA HISTORICAL SOCIETY

THE UNIVERSITY PRESS OF VIRGINIA

Charlottesville   1965

Published with the assistance of the
Old Dominion Foundation

© *1965 by the Virginia Historical Society*

First Published 1965
The University Press of Virginia
Library of Congress Catalog Card Number: 65–23459
Printed in the United States of America

PREFACE

The Reverend John Clayton was the rector of James City Parish, Virginia, from 1684 until 1686, and he continued his clerical career in England and Ireland until his death in 1725. He is remembered, however, for his scientific, rather than his clerical, accomplishments. He had been educated at Oxford and had a record of scientific investigation in England before he came to North America. While in Virginia he made extensive observations of natural phenomena, which he communicated at various times to scientists in England, especially to Robert Boyle, Nehemiah Grew, and other members of the Royal Society of London. These observations were presumably influential in establishing a picture of the New World in European minds. Most of them have been published; a few are still in manuscript. The collection of his known scientific writing in one volume will, it is hoped, prove both interesting and useful to those concerned with early American science.

The only biography of Clayton is Walter T. Layton's *The Discoverer of Gas Lighting, Notes on the Life and Work of the Reverend John Clayton, D.D., 1657–1725* (London, 1926). This well-written book is unfortunately now out of print. We acknowledge with pleasure our indebtedness to it, especially for material concerning Clayton's immediate family and ministry.

It is quite impossible to investigate one John Clayton without encountering quite a number of others. The problem lies in identifying the particular man involved in each case. During the summer of 1961 the editors were privileged to work in a number of European libraries, primarily seeking information concerning John Clayton (1694–1773), the botanist, but actually gathering material relating to his father, grandfather, and cousin, all of the same name. We had been pleased to receive a suggestion from the Virginia Historical Society that we undertake to edit the scientific writings of the Reverend John Clayton, a project originally started by Dr. Conway Zirkle, who found that he was unable to continue it. We are indebted to both Dr. Zirkle and the Virginia Historical Society for the opportunity of carrying out this project. We should like to express our appreciation to the American Philosophical Society, whose generous grant assisted with the expenses of that summer in Europe, and to the Research Council of the University of North Carolina at Greensboro, whose grants have helped with other expenses.

Permission to publish manuscript materials has been kindly given by the trustees of the British Museum; the Board of Trinity College, Dublin; and the librarian of the Royal Society of London. Copyright of the documents remains the property of these institutions. The librarian of the College of William and Mary has kindly given permission to reproduce Clayton's map of Jamestown.

A great number of people have assisted us in many ways, and it is a pleasure to acknowledge our indebtedness to them, especially to Dr. John Barry, Society of Genealogists, Dublin; Mr. A. Carrick, Liverpool Record Office, Liverpool; Mr. Desmond Clarke, librarian and secretary of the Royal Dublin Society, Ball's Bridge, Dublin; Dr. Joseph Ewan, Tulane University; Miss A. G. Foster, librarian, Yorkshire Archaeological Society, Leeds; Mr. R. Sharpe France, county archivist, Lancashire Record Office, Preston, Lancashire; Mrs. A. Rupert Hall (Marie Boas), Indiana University; Mr. Paul D. A. Harvey, Department of Manuscripts, the British Museum; Dr. Charles E. Hatch, Jr., chief park historian, Colonial National Historical Park, Yorktown; Mr. R. Highfield, librarian, Merton College, Oxford; Mr. Theo Hoppen, Department of History, University College, Dublin; Dr. I. Kaye, librarian, The Royal Society of London; Mr. John L. Lochhead, librarian, The Mariners' Museum, Newport News; Mr. Alf MacLochlain, National Library, Dublin; Dr. R. E. W. Maddison, Heston, Middlesex; Mr. William O'Sullivan, archivist, Trinity College, Dublin; Mr. M. Pollard, deputy librarian, Archbishop Marsh's Library, Dublin; Mr. Richard G. Proby, Elton Hall, Peterborough; Mr. J. D. H. Widoess, librarian, Royal College of Surgeons in Ireland, Dublin; and Miss Geraldine Willis, librarian, The Representative Body of the Church of Ireland, Dublin.

It has been our privilege to work in a number of libraries where many members of the staff have been extremely helpful. We should like to thank particularly the Baker Library, Dartmouth College; the Institute of Historical Research, University of London; the libraries of the University of North Carolina at Greensboro and Chapel Hill; the Bodleian Library, University of Oxford; the Library of Trinity College, Dublin; and the Alderman Library, University of Virginia.

EDMUND BERKELEY
DOROTHY SMITH BERKELEY

University of North Carolina at Greensboro
April 5, 1965

CONTENTS

ILLUSTRATIONS

BIOGRAPHICAL SKETCH OF THE REVEREND JOHN CLAYTON

In the spring of 1684, John Clayton, newly arrived at Jamestown, was gratified to receive a special order from the governor and Council to preach a sermon for the meeting of the Assembly. He was but twenty-seven and, although he had received his M.A. from Oxford two years earlier, he was not yet accustomed to the respect with which Virginians treated him, as he wrote in a letter in April of that year.[1] This letter and others of his subsequent writings comprise the major part of this volume. They provide a fascinating commentary, by a well-trained scientist, on Virginia in the late seventeenth century. They may, perhaps, be more interesting if the reader has some prior acquaintance with their author.

EARLY LIFE AND EDUCATION

John Clayton was born in the year 1657,[2] the third son of Robert Clayton, of Old Crooke and Fulwood, estates in Lanca-

[1] B.M., Sloane MSS 1008, f. 334–35. See p. 3, n. 1, below.

[2] John Foster, *Alumni Oxonienses, 1500–1714* (London, 1891). University of Oxford alumni records state that Clayton matriculated at St. Alban Hall at age 17 in 1674; *ergo*, he must have been born sometime in the year 1657. They are in error in regard to his father, whom they name Richard. See *The Visitation of . . . Lancashire, . . . 1664–5, by Sir William Dugdale,* ed. F. R. Raines (Chetham Society, *Remains, Historical & Literary . . . ,* Vol. LXXXIV [Manchester, 1872]), p. 85. The Clayton family is also mentioned by Edward Baines in *The History of the County Palatine and Duchy of Lancaster,* ed. James Croston (London, 1893), V, 433.

shire, a few miles from the village of Preston. Fulwood had been one of five great forests in Lancashire from which King John had granted to the burgesses of Preston the right of cutting wood to build their town. It was in a farming community, and a fairly prosperous one in the seventeenth century. John's family was one of some means and distinction, descended from the Claytons of Yorkshire. His uncle, Thomas Clayton, was an alderman of Liverpool for many years and mayor in 1680.[3] A contemporary relative, although somewhat distant, was Sir John Clayton, of London, member of the Privy Chamber under William III and one of the original fellows of the Royal Society of London. Sir John's son, John, was attorney-general of Virginia from 1713 until 1737, and his grandson, also John, was the well-known botanist, who has long been confused with the parson. Both were able scientists who wrote about the flora and fauna of Virginia.[4]

Clayton's mother was Eleanor, daughter of John Atherton. Her paternal grandfather, John, and her great-grandfather of the same name, had held office as high sheriff and had been members of Parliament. Her nephew, Richard Atherton, Clayton's first cousin and friend, had a distinguished career, representing Liverpool in Parliament 1677–79 and 1685. In 1684 he was elected mayor and also was knighted by Charles II.[5]

Clayton's immediate family was a large one. He had two older brothers, Thomas and William, and a younger brother, Richard, as well as five sisters. Thomas matriculated at Mag-

---

[3] W. T. Layton, *The Discoverer of Gas Lighting, Notes of the Life and Work of the Reverend John Clayton, D.D., 1657–1725* (London, 1926), p. 6.

[4] This branch likewise descended from the Yorkshire Claytons. See Edmund Berkeley and D. S. Berkeley, *John Clayton, Pioneer of American Botany* (Chapel Hill, N.C., 1963), pp. 7–17.

[5] William Farrer and John Brownbill (eds.), *Victoria History of Lancashire* (London, 1907–14), III, 437.

dalen Hall, Oxford, in 1667 and later studied law. William went into business in Liverpool, became mayor in 1689, and represented the city in Parliament for many years.[6] Their father appears to have sold Old Crooke sometime prior to 1688, moving his family to Liverpool but retaining the Fulwood estates.[7]

Some indication of the family character and prosperity may be had from the fact that John, a third son, was sent to Oxford. He matriculated at St. Alban Hall, July 17, 1674. The principal at that time was Dr. Narcissus Marsh (1638–1713), who seems to have had a strong influence on him.[8] Clayton's second son was named Narcissus, and many years later Clayton dedicated a sermon to Marsh in appreciation of having had the privilege of studying under his direction. Among Marsh's many interests were mathematics and acoustics. It is noteworthy that Clayton also developed some competence in the latter field.

Sometime in the succeeding four years Clayton transferred from St. Alban Hall to nearby Merton College. The warden of Merton was Sir Thomas Clayton,[9] perhaps a relative, but no

[6] Gerard Noel, *Members of Parliament* (London, 1878). There are letters of William Clayton and references to him among *The Norris Papers,* edited by Thomas Heywood (Chetham Society, *Remains, Historical & Literary . . . ,* Vol. IX [Manchester, 1846]).

[7] Layton, *Discoverer of Gas Lighting,* 29. Robert Clayton died January 29, 1691, and was buried at the Church of St. Nicholas in Liverpool. His wife, who had died in 1681, was buried in Broughton Churchyard near Preston (*ibid.,* p. 29).

[8] Marsh had taken office in May of the previous year. According to Anthony à Wood, he "made it [St. Alban Hall] flourish, kept up a severe discipline . . . kept up a weekly meeting for music" (Andrew Clark [ed.], *The Life and Times of Anthony Wood, Antiquary of Oxford, 1632–1695* [Oxford, 1892], II, 264). Marsh became provost of Trinity College, Dublin, January 24, 1678/9, and shortly afterward was appointed to a bishopric.

[9] It is unfortunate that most of the information concerning Sir Thomas is contained in the *Life and Times* of Anthony à Wood, who disliked him intensely, possibly because the warden had reported him as being "Popishly

connection has been established. The scientific emphasis was strong at Merton. Not only was Sir Thomas Clayton a professor of medicine, but he followed a series of wardens who were prominent medical men.[10] Medicine was then a rather wide field, encompassing most of science, and Oxford was well known for its "scientific climate."[11] Clayton absorbed much of the enthusiasm for science which prevailed there, especially for the experimental approach. He became very proficient, not only in planning experiments, but also in designing and constructing the apparatus with which he carried them out.

Official records of Oxford do not indicate that Clayton received an M.D. degree, although he has been thought to have had one,[12] but he did receive a bachelor's degree in 1678 and a master's degree in 1682. That he received considerable medical training, later practicing medicine to some extent, is evident from his writings.

Although there is little information concerning Clayton's location and principal occupation in the interval between his leaving Oxford and his departure for Virginia, part of his time

---

affected" (Clark, *Anthony Wood*, II, 440). Nonetheless Wood gives an amusing picture of Sir Thomas' family. He resented the fact that Dr. Clayton moved his wife and family into college property, and "put the college to unnecessary charges, and very frivolous expenses, among which were a large looking glass, for her to see her ugly face, and body to the middle, and perhaps lower. . . . The said bursar . . . hath several times told me, that either he (the Warden) or his lady do invent, and sit thinking how to put the college to charge" (*ibid.*, II, 398).

[10] "Merton had become famous for medicine in the Late Middle Ages (it supplied Gaddesden, physician to Edward II & author of the Rosa Medicine). In the 16th. John Chambre, Warden was physician . . . & founded the Barber Surgeons. In the 17th. C. four Wardens were doctors: William Harvey, physician to Charles I, Warden 1645–6, Jonathan Goddard, physician to Cromwell, Warden 1651–60, and Sir Thomas Clayton . . . & Richard Lydall 1693" (personal communication from R. Highfield, librarian of Merton College).

[11] R. T. Gunther, *Early Science in Oxford* (Oxford, 1920–45), I, 9–17, 288.

[12] Gregson mentioned that William Clayton had "a brother, a Doctor in Medicine in Dublin" according to Heywood, *Norris Papers*, p. 51.

was occupied with some serious scientific experimentation, but unfortunately all of his records of these experiments were lost on his way to Virginia. In the second of his two surviving letters to Robert Boyle, he referred to one series of experiments involving the use of a "New Digester."[13]

The term "Digester" may call for some explanation. A Frenchman, Denis Papin, M.D. (who is credited with developing the first cylinder and piston steam engine) while assisting Robert Boyle with some experiments, noted that when steam was prevented from escaping, it raised the temperature of the container which held it above the boiling point of water. He found that the higher temperatures obtained in this way cooked many things more rapidly than did ordinary boiling. He devised special containers for this purpose, which he called "Digesters." Thus was born the prototype of the modern pressure cooker or autoclave. Since his invention of the safety valve came later, it is remarkable that Dr. Papin lived long enough to report his invention. He did, however, present and demonstrate one to the Royal Society of London. The Society was very favorably impressed and encouraged him to publish an account of his discoveries, which he did in 1681 as "A New Digester or Engine for softening bones, containing the description of its make and use in these particulars, viz., Cookery, Chymistry and Dying. With an account of the Price a good big Engine will cost, and of the Profit it will afford." The Digester became something of a sensation, so much so that Papin announced: "I will let people see the Machine try'd once a week in Blackfriars."[14] So impressed were the members

[13] See p. 11, below.
[14] C. R. Weld, *History of the Royal Society* (London, 1848), II, 286. Papin apparently served as a temporary curator of the Society in 1684. He was paid 30 pounds a year to be certain that experiments were prepared for each meeting. In 1687 he left England to become professor of mathematics at the University of Marburg (*ibid.*, pp. 287–89).

of the Royal Society that they partook of an entire meal prepared in the Digester on March 12, 1682. Fortunately John Evelyn recorded the event for posterity.

I went this afternoone with severall of ye R. S. to a supper wch was all dress'd, both fish and flesh, in *Mor Papin's Digestors,* by which the hardest bones of beefe itselfe, and mutton, were made as soft as cheese, without water or other liquor, and with lesse than 8 ounces of coales, producing an incredible quantity of gravy; and for close of all a jelly made of ye bones of beef, the best for clearness and good relish, and the most delicious that I had ever seene or tasted. We eat pike and other fish bones, and all without impediment; but nothing exceeded the pigeons, which tasted just as if bak'd in a pie, all these being stew'd in their own juice, without any addition of water save what swam about the Digester as *in balneo,* the natural juice of all these provisions acting on the grosser substances, reduc'd the hardest bones to tendernesse. . . . This philosophical supper caus'd much mirth amongst us, and exceedingly pleas'd all ye company.[15]

John Clayton made extensive experiments with Digesters soon after this. He made improvements in their design and used them to make studies of gas pressure before Boyle's Law was widely known.

In another area of science Clayton was making experiments of medical significance, studying the specific gravities and related properties of liquids, especially urines. He had special "glasses" blown in various sizes for use in these experiments, and he discussed the usefulness of such information in medical diagnosis. These studies, too, were interrupted by his journey to Virginia, but were later resumed.

No record has been found of Clayton's ordination. It probably took place after he received his master's degree in

---

[15] John Evelyn, *Memoirs Illustrative of the Life and Writings of John Evelyn, Esq. F.R.S.,* ed. William Bray (London, 1818), I, 509.

1682, but it could have been earlier. The church offered security, which scientific careers did not, and was no longer a bar to the pursuit of scientific interests. A number of scientifically trained men were ordained at this time. The Bishop of London, Henry Compton, who was responsible for ministerial appointments for James City parish, had a keen interest in botany. His gardens at Fulham Palace were famous for their introduced plants. Among the clergymen-botanists sent to America at this time were the Reverend Hugh Jones and the Reverend John Banister.

The experimental work for which Clayton has been best known, and which has been considered to be his most important scientific contribution, was probably done just prior to his departure for Virginia, but can only be dated with certainty as being before July 1687, when he wrote an account of it to Boyle. This was his study of natural coal gas at Wigan, in Lancashire. Wigan was a coal-mining town south of Preston. Clayton's uncle, Thomas Clayton,[16] owned the manor of Adlington there. One of the local curiosities of Wigan was a natural gas "spring," which had burned at intervals over a period of years and attracted a good deal of local attention. It had been reported to the Royal Society of London, as all such phenomena were sooner or later. One Thomas Shirley had visited it in 1659, and his description of it appeared in the *Philosophical Transactions* for 1667.[17] Whether or not Clayton was familiar with Shirley's account is not important. He had reason to visit Wigan to see his uncle and would have heard of the gas. He went well beyond Shirley in that he took samples of nearby coal, distilled them, and produced gas and

[16] Layton, *Discoverer of Gas Lighting*, pp. 6–7.
[17] It was entitled "Description of a Well and Earth in Lancashire Taking Fire by a Candle approached to it" (II [1667], 482–84). Shirley noted that the spring was located 30 or 40 yards from a coal pit.

tar. He then demonstrated that the gas was insoluble in
water, as well as inflammable, and that it could be stored.
Layton has credited him with being the discoverer of gas
lighting and has presented a well-documented case to show
that, while William Murdoch first lighted his house with coal
gas in 1792, "about half a century before Murdoch's experiment a communication had been received and filed by the
Royal Society concerning a discovery made by a clergyman
who distilled coal and lighted the gas produced from it more
than a century before 1792, in fact not later than 1688, and
possibly earlier."[18] He goes on to point out that actually this
experiment had been referred to by Clayton in one of his
letters concerning Virginia, written to the Royal Society in
May 1688 and published by them in 1693.[19]

Although Clayton has been assumed to have gone to Virginia primarily as a clergyman, albeit one with some interest in
science, he was also a well-trained scientist, with a considerable
experience of serious research behind him. It is not surprising that he was able to make as many intelligent and important
observations as he did there.

TWO YEARS IN VIRGINIA

Early in January of 1684 Clayton sailed from England on the
ship "Judith," Captain Trim in command. The trip to Virginia lasted twelve weeks, in the course of which Clayton made
a number of scientific observations which he later reported to
the Royal Society. These included examinations of marine

[18] Layton, *Discoverer of Gas Lighting,* pp. 1–2.

[19] Layton's statement that the Royal Society had received Clayton's account
"half a century before Murdoch's experiment" may be puzzling. Clayton
himself did not send his account to the Royal Society. His son Robert sent
this and other experiments which he found among his father's papers to the
Royal Society in 1739. The paper was not published until 1740. If Layton
had been familiar with the full text of Clayton's letter to Boyle, he might
have said not later than 1687, rather than 1688.

animals, such as the Portuguese man-of-war, and an attempt to study ocean currents. Such activities were possible while the ship was becalmed. More important at the time was his ability to apply sound reasoning and a speaking trumpet of his own design to helping Captain Trim's crew to find a dangerous leak which they had been unable to locate.

It is difficult to determine just what Clayton found at Jamestown upon his arrival. Whatever buildings were there were new, for the entire town, consisting of twelve brick houses, a number of frame houses, the church, and the statehouse, had been burned by Nathaniel Bacon on September 19, 1676.[1] Some rebuilding had certainly been done, but just how much is not clear. The new statehouse (the fourth) was built a year later.[2]

Clayton's surviving writings make no comment on churches in Virginia. The first church at Jamestown had been merely an awning under the trees, and later buildings had not been immune to fire.[3] The church had been rebuilt since the fire of 1676 and did not differ a great deal from contemporary rural churches in England. Its dimensions were approximately twenty-two feet by fifty feet, not including the three-foot walls of English bonded brick. The tower was a full thirty feet tall, rising three stories, each marked by double courses of Flemish bond. The interior of the church was plastered, and the center aisle was paved with brick. The transverse aisle was also of brick and enclosed the tombstone of the Reverend John Clougher, who died in 1684, and was presumably Clayton's immediate predecessor. The furnishings of the church were probably very much like those of the second one, described by

---

[1] R. L. Morton, *Colonial Virginia* (Chapel Hill, N.C., 1960), I, 270.
[2] H. C. Forman, *Jamestown and St. Mary's* (Baltimore, 1938), pp. 172–73.
[3] Bishop William Meade, *Old Churches, Ministers, and Families of Virginia* (Philadelphia, 1861), I, 69.

Strachey as having a chancel of cedar, altar of black walnut, and cedar pulpit and pews. The graveyard was approximately one-half acre of ground enclosed by a brick wall.[4] The silver chalice with patten which Clayton used for Communion services was probably one that is still in existence, which bears the inscription, "Ex Dono Jacobi Morrison Armigere, A D 1661."[5]

James City Parish was the court church of Virginia until the capital was moved to Williamsburg in 1699, when it became an ordinary parish. It included part of the mainland on the river's northern bank as well as the island of Jamestown.[6] Because of its comparative importance, James City's rectors were chosen with care, and the roll of previous ministers included quite a few distinguished men, such as Richard Hakluyt, Robert Hunt, and Hawte Wyatt, brother of Governor Sir Francis Wyatt.[7]

Clayton seems to have made a favorable impression upon the governor and burgesses. At any rate, he received a fairly liberal payment for his services. On Thursday, the fifteenth of May, the *Journal* of the House of Burgesses records, "The petition of Mr. *John Clayton* Clerke for allowance for his Attendance at *James Citty* this Assembly by his Excellencies special Order. The House of Burgesses are of opinion he merits five pounds *ster.* to be paid out of the Revenue of two shillings P hogshead, according to Act of Assembly."[8]

From Clayton's later writings we learn that he made his

[4] Forman, *Jamestown*, pp. 157–60. The Colonial Dames have been responsible for the reconstruction of the church, based on St. Luke's at Smithfield.

[5] Meade, *Old Churches*, I, 96.

[6] G. MacL. Brydon, "Historic Parishes, I. James City Parish in Virginia," *Historical Magazine of the Protestant Episcopal Church*, IX (1942), 69.

[7] E. L. Goodwin, *The Colonial Church in Virginia* (London, 1927), p. 81.

[8] H. R. McIlwaine (ed.), *Journals of the House of Burgesses of Virginia, 1659/60–1693* (Richmond, 1914), p. 226.

home at, or near, Jamestown, on a plantation where tobacco was raised. He never identified the family, although he mentions a visit from his landlady after his return to England. The impression is conveyed that she was a widow, since he records that he gave her a great deal of advice concerning the running of the plantation and he never mentions her husband.

Clayton's clerical duties were not arduous enough to prevent him from engaging in many other activities. One of his keen interests was agriculture. He was frankly shocked to find that Englishmen could be as bad farmers as he found them to be. Having no understanding of the drainage of low swampy ground, they cultivated only the high ground, which soon became depleted and more had to be cleared. They took little care of their livestock, leaving the animals to shift for themselves and losing many as a result. They continued to prepare their tobacco seedbeds as they always had, in spite of losses from insects and poor growth of seedlings. He set about trying to educate them with more enthusiasm than tact and succeeded only in antagonizing them. The overseer on the plantation where he lived suggested that Clayton knew more about preparing sermons than he did about farming and should stick to the former. Clayton was not content merely to criticize. He took men and drained a swamp. He took tobacco seed and produced five times as many usable seedlings in the same-sized plot that others were using. Unfortunately not even demonstration seemed to impress many of the Virginians.

Nothing in Clayton's writings indicates definitely whether he had planned permanent residence in Virginia or whether he knew himself to be on temporary assignment. One is inclined toward the latter view by the astonishing amount of observation and study that he accomplished in a comparatively short time. This may have been inherent in his makeup, but other hints support the view that he did not expect to remain long. There can be no doubt that he went to Virginia with the intention of making serious scientific investigations. He prepared himself well for doing so and went provided with microscopes, barometers, thermometers, and chemical instruments of various sorts. These included the "glasses" which he had had specially blown for use in making studies of the specific gravities and other properties of liquids. He also took with him reference books and all of his own notes on the experimental work he had been doing in England. In other words, everything he felt that he might have difficulty in obtaining in Virginia, he took with him. All of this careful preparation went for nought when Captain Winn's ship, on which they followed him, was lost.[9]

The loss of all that he had planned to work with not only handicapped Clayton, but it discouraged him so much that he failed to make as many written notes as he might have done, and this he had cause to regret later. Had he considered himself on a permanent or long assignment, he would presumably have attempted to replace what he had lost from England.[10] In true scientific fashion, when he later reported his observations at the request of the Royal Society, he warned against trusting too much to his memory of them. Despite this, even after a lapse of several years he was able to relate extensive and frequently detailed observations of plants, ani-

[9] A Captain John Wynn was often mentioned by William Byrd I before and after 1684, so it seems unlikely that he was in command of the ship to which Clayton entrusted his precious belongings (W. G. Stanard [ed.], "Letters of William Byrd, First," *Va. Mag. Hist. Biog.*, XXIV [1916], 226–36 *passim*).

[10] The only known exception was some books which Clayton ordered sent over from England by Perry and Lane in 1684 (Elizabeth Donnan, "Eighteenth Century English Merchants: Micajah Perry," *Jour. Econ. Bus. Hist.*, IV [November, 1931], 70–89).

mals, soils, waters, weather, and Indians, which are surprisingly accurate in the cases we can check. He was a good listener and acquired a great deal of information from the people he met. That he got some misinformation is not surprising. He was aware of the danger and warned against it. He performed such experiments as he could and made some attempts to replace locally his lost equipment. Thus he spoke of using local clay to make some very satisfactory crucibles. He mentioned distilling plants, so he must have contrived a still. He collected both flora and fauna extensively. He spoke of collecting some three hundred different herbs that he thought unknown in Europe – no small accomplishment if even approximately correct. The bad luck which beset him continued when all of his large collection of bird specimens was thrown out during his critical illness because a few items became a bit odoriferous!

Science was far less specialized in Clayton's day than it has become since. The truly curious man felt less hesitation in exploring any aspect of natural history. Even fifty years after Clayton visited Virginia, Peter Shaw (editing Boyle's works) could write:

Natural History seems at present to lie under some Disgrace upon account of the small Benefit that is presumed to arise from the Study of it. . . . But if any Man has a despicable opinion of Natural History in general, let him look upon it in that View wherein Mr. Boyle considered it; for here, as in every Thing else, our excellent Author has regarded Usefullness and the Benefit of Mankind. Natural History, as managed by him, has no superfluous Branches.[11]

It is perhaps significant that Clayton sensed a kindred spirit when, in one of his two surviving letters written from James-

[11] Peter Shaw (ed.), *The Philosophical Works of the Honourable Robert Boyle Esq.* (London, 1725) , III, 3.

town, he introduced himself to the great Robert Boyle and reported to him observations which he correctly assumed that Boyle would like to know.

On the west side of Chesapeake Bay, just north of the mouth of the Potomac River, was St. Mary's City, capital of Maryland. Although some distance from Jamestown, the bay provided communication.[12]   Thus it is not too surprising that Clayton met, not long after his arrival in Virginia, Colonel and Mrs. William Digges, who had bought a plantation near St. Mary's in 1680.   Digges was a son of the former Virginia governor, Edward Digges, and was deputy governor of Maryland from 1684 to 1688.   His wife was Elizabeth, daughter of Henry Sewall, secretary of Maryland.   Her widowed mother had married as her second husband Charles Calvert (1637–1715), the third Lord Baltimore.   In addition to the daughter Elizabeth, there had been a son, Nicholas Sewall, and it was Susanna, wife of Nicholas, who provided the incident which Clayton reported to Boyle.[13]   Boyle had written extensively on matters relating to luminescence.

It is not surprising that, as rector at Jamestown, Clayton was soon on cordial terms with many of the most prominent people of the colony.   These included the governor, Lord Howard of Effingham (1643–95), who had arrived from England only in February 1684, and Secretary of State Nicholas Spencer, whom he knew very well.   Spencer had been appointed president of the Council and acting governor at Lord Culpeper's departure the previous year.[14]   Upon the arrival of Effingham, he became secretary of the colony.   Another friend was William Sherwood.   He was one of Virginia's two wealthiest planters, had

[12] Forman, *Jamestown*, p. viii.
[13] *Ibid.*, pp. 235–36.
[14] Morton, *Colonial Virginia*, I, 309.

been attorney-general (1678–80), and was a widely respected barrister. Four years previously Sherwood had built a house on the ruins of that of John Knowles, and its great "Hall" had been used for meetings of the Council. One-and-a-half stories in height, the house had a commodious cellar of two sixteen-by-seventeen-foot rooms. In one of them was a fireplace seven feet wide and three feet deep. In recent excavations of the site plaster showing evidence of colored frescoes and parquetry in relief was found.[15] Sherwood was the owner of the 150-acre swamp running diagonally across Jamestown Island which Clayton recommended draining. Many of Clayton's friends and acquaintances received only passing mention in his letters or writings: Ralph Wormeley, member of the Council; Colonel Nicholas Smith, of the Isle of Wight, whose house was robbed by pirates in March 1685;[16] Colonel (Thomas?) Ballard; and Colonels Troop and Coles. He had little respect for the knowledge of members of the medical profession in Virginia and only mentions one by name, a Dr. Lee, and a second by initial, Dr. A., whose death by lightning he describes.

One person who should have been very helpful to Clayton was the Reverend John Banister, rector of Charles City. They would have had much in common. Banister, too, was an able scientist as well as a clergyman, and he had preceded Clayton to Virginia by several years. He was by this time well along with the collection of plants which eventually appeared in print as the *Catalogus Plantarum in Virginia Observatarum.*[17]

[15] Forman, *Jamestown*, p. 118.

[16] H. R. McIlwaine (ed.), *Executive Journals of the Council of Colonial Virginia* (Richmond, 1925), I, 68.

[17] Banister's writings and papers have been edited by Dr. and Mrs. Joseph Ewan, of Tulane University, and should be shortly in press. The *Catalogus* was published in John Ray, *Historia Plantarum* (London, 1686–), pp. 1927 ff.

The two men met, since Clayton records their discussion of an evolutionary problem and the cicada. How much they saw of each other is not clear. Probably it was not a great deal, since there are only the two references to Banister in Clayton's writings.

Perhaps Clayton's most congenial friend, with whom he spent quite a bit of time, was William Byrd I. He was the son of a London goldsmith, who had come to Virginia about 1670. He had inherited the estate of his uncle, Thomas Stegg. His maternal grandfather, Captain Thomas Stegg, had been trading on the James River as early as 1637, and Byrd was continuing the trade.[18] Where Richmond is today, Byrd built his home, Belvidere, which Andrew Burnaby described in 1759 as being "as romantic and elegant as anything" he had ever seen.[19] It was, nonetheless, rather lonesome, and Byrd maintained an apartment at Jamestown. It was doubtless here that Clayton made his acquaintance. He acquired a great deal of information from Byrd concerning Virginia, and he was able to supply much of current interest from England. Byrd may well have been the person who introduced him to the Indians, whose customs he studied in some detail. Byrd's trade with them provided him more direct contact than was enjoyed by most of the colonists. It was during Clayton's stay in Virginia that Byrd and Edmund Jenings were appointed coagents to go to Albany, New York, to ratify the articles of the Indian Treaty that Effingham had negotiated.[20]

It may well have been through Byrd that Clayton became acquainted with some member or members of the Batts and Fallam expedition, which made the first documented crossing

---

[18] Morton, *Colonial Virginia*, II, 426.

[19] *Travels through the Middle Settlements in North-America* (Ithaca, N.Y., 1960; reprint of the 1775 London edition), p. 9.

[20] McIlwaine, *Executive Journals*, I, 72.

of the Appalachian Mountains.[21]   Certainly, he discussed some
aspects of it with Byrd.   General Abraham Wood, who was responsible for the exploration, is thought to have died about
1680, although the date is not known.   Byrd had land near
Wood's trading post at Fort Henry and was exploring with a
company of his own at the same time that Thomas Batts and
Robert Fallam were making their journey.   Somehow Clayton
obtained access to the journal kept by the party and took the
time to copy it in detail, correctly considering it to be an important document.

Although Tidewater Virginia had now been settled continuously for more than half a century, very little was known
concerning the interior.   Traders such as Stegg, and later Byrd
and Wood, were sending pack-horse trading expeditions well
beyond tidewater into the piedmont, both north and south,
but much mystery still surrounded the question of the extent
of the unknown territory to the west.   The somewhat vague
answers obtained to questions asked of friendly Indians only
served to add to the confusion and increase the rumors of a
wondrous sea and hints of possible treasure.   One recorded
account suggested that "the sea of China and the Indies" was
just ten days' journey beyond the source of the James River.[22]
One might have expected early exploration, but it was not an
easy undertaking.   The Batts and Fallam journal makes clear
some of the problems involved.   In 1650 Edward Bland had
led an expedition as far west as the present-day location of
Clarksville, Virginia.   Abraham Wood had been a member of
Bland's party.   Bland died in 1653, before undertaking an-

[21] It is also possible that Sir William Berkeley's widow permitted Clayton to
copy the account from the late governor's papers. The Batts and Fallam
journal is given on p. 68, below.
[22] In C. W. Alvord and Lee Bidgood (eds.), *The First Explorations of the
Trans-Allegheny Region by the Virginians, 1650–1674* (Cleveland, 1912),
p. 47.

other journey, but others were interested in exploring beyond Bland's stopping point. Governor Berkeley was very much interested in this exploration. He gave encouragement to a German physician, John Lederer, who is credited with being the first person to discover the Valley of Virginia, which he saw from the top of the Blue Ridge Mountains in 1669. Berkeley sent an expedition in 1670 which did not cross these mountains. Since Batts and Fallam found initials carved on trees, they presumably were not the first white men to cross the Allegheny divide, but the carvers of the initials seem to have left no other record of themselves. Thus, Batts and Fallam provided the first written record.[23]

There is no indication that Clayton did any exploring beyond fairly well-settled portions of Virginia. He wrote to Boyle that he would be happy to ride two or even three hundred miles to seek any information which he might desire, but nothing in his writings suggests that he went farther from Jamestown than Byrd's home at the Falls of the James; he definitely did go there. He became thoroughly familiar with the settled areas including Gloucester, Isle of Wight, Nansemond, Charles City, and New Kent. Very little which he might have been expected to observe in this tidewater area escaped him. He has left us an interesting picture of his conferences with Indians concerning remedies, his botanizing expeditions in which he sought simples, and his habit of carrying roots around in his pockets to nibble on and observe the effects, if any.

RETURN TO ENGLAND

In May of 1686 Clayton sailed from Virginia for England, taking with him some drawings of plants, probably some collections, and certainly a vast fund of information. Once

[23] *Ibid.*, pp. 46–69; Morton. *Colonial Virginia*, I, 200–2.

again he improved the time aboard ship by making scientific observations of various sorts. These ranged from the dissection of sea turtles to the habits of sea birds and the size of icebergs. He arrived in England sometime in late summer.

The year following his return to England was spent in Huntingdonshire. He is presumed to have had a church there, but exactly where is not known. One possibility might be the Church of All Saints, Buckworth. In 1666 the third Duke of Richmond had conveyed the manor and advowson there to John Backwell and Robert Clayton.[1] This Clayton may have been a relative, even possibly his father, but there is no evidence to support the speculation.

During his year in Huntingdonshire he made the acquaintance of Sir Thomas Proby, formerly of Buckinghamshire, grandson of Sir Peter Proby, who had been lord mayor of London in 1622–23. The Probys had purchased Elton Hall in 1617. Sir Thomas Proby had made extensive renovations of the old house when he came to live there. The original building was constructed in 1477.[2] Proby expressed an interest in Clayton's new Digester, and the latter wrote several accounts of the demonstration which he gave for him.

Sometime during his year in Huntingdonshire Clayton made a trip to London. All that we know about it is that it was the occasion for his meeting Robert Boyle. Only two letters to Boyle are known, the first from Jamestown and a second written soon after he left Huntingdonshire in July 1687. Boyle had long been well acquainted with Clayton's kinsman, Sir John Clayton, who, like himself, was an original fellow of the Royal Society. Boyle had been much interested

[1] William Page, Granville Proby, and S. I. Ladds (eds.), *The Victoria History of the County of Huntingdon* (Waterloo, Eng., 1930–36), I, 24.

[2] *Ibid.*, III, 154–60. Richard G. Proby, Esq., of Elton Hall, states that he knows of no surviving correspondence between his ancestor and Clayton. His elder brother was one of the editors of *The Victoria History*.

in a gem which Sir John had acquired in Italy, along with various items related to his interest in alchemy. He wrote to Sir Robert Moray in 1663, "As I was just going out of town, hearing that an ingenious gentleman of my acquaintance, lately returned from Italy, had a diamond, that being rubbed, would shine in the dark, and that he was not far off; I snatched time from my occasions to make him a visit."[3] Possibly the diamond played some part in Clayton's being knighted, November 17, 1664, for Boyle later wrote that he had "a good while since restored to Mr. Clayton the stone, which, though it be now in the hands of a prince, that so highly deserves by understanding them, the greatest curiosities."[4] Boyle published his *Observations made October 27, 1663 about Mr. Clayton's Diamond and read before the Royal Society the day following,* along with his *Experiments and Considerations touching Colours,* at London in 1663.[5]

It seems probable that the Reverend John Clayton saw Boyle in the late spring of 1687. There can be no doubt that he was cordially received and made a very favorable impression on Boyle, spending some hours with him. Clayton referred to being present during experiments with the "snake stones" which had been given Boyle by James II. Boyle was extremely interested in a speaking trumpet which Clayton had designed and which had been used to good advantage on his voyage to Virginia. He requested a drawing of it that he might present it to the king. Clayton's Virginia experiences must have fascinated Boyle, and it is possible that the latter's concern for the Indians may have been aroused then. Boyle's will left sufficient funds to establish a school for the instruction

[3] Thomas Birch (ed.), *The Works of the Honourable Robert Boyle* (London, 1772), I, 789.

[4] *Ibid.,* I, 790. A further reference to the "Monarch" leaves little doubt that the prince was Charles II.

[5] *Ibid.,* I, 796–99.

of nine or ten Indian children at Williamsburg.[6] It is true that he had always been interested in such matters and Charles II had appointed him governor of the Corporation for Propagating the Gospel in colonial America,[7] which office he eventually was forced to resign because of ill health. The clergyman Clayton found much in common with this man who was described by Gilbert Burnet as "highly charitable; and was a mortified and self-denied man, that delighted in nothing so much as in the doing good. He neglected his person, despised the world, and lived abstracted from all pleasures, designs and interests."[8] Boyle's interest in education and his Irish connections may have influenced Clayton in his later career.

The fact that Clayton spent some time with Boyle is noteworthy, because it was at a time when visitors had become such a problem to Boyle that he found it necessary to limit the days and hours during which he would receive people. It was a practice of Boyle to present series of questions about scientific problems which concerned him to friends whom he thought capable of shedding some light on the subject. It was in answer to a list of twenty-two such "Quaeres" that Clayton wrote his second letter. Boyle had evidently written following Clayton's visit, sending them. Clayton's reply gives our finest account of some of his research. Perhaps the best measure of Clayton's impression on Boyle is that the latter had

---

[6] W. S. Perry, *Historical Collections Relating to the American Colonial Church* (Hartford, 1870), I, 123, 300, 306, 327. For further details, see H. L. Ganter, "Some Notes on the Charity of the Honourable Robert Boyle, Esq. of the City of London, Deceased" (*William and Mary Quarterly*, ser. 2, XV [1935], 1–39).

[7] According to his will (Birch, *Boyle*, I, clviii–clxxi).

[8] *History of His Own Time* (London, 1724), I, 198. Particularly helpful for the study of Boyle's influence are Marie Boas, *Robert Boyle and Seventeenth-Century Chemistry* (Cambridge, 1958) and M. S. Fisher, *Robert Boyle, Devout Naturalist, A Study in Science and Religion in the Seventeenth Century* (Philadelphia, 1945).

promised to provide a code which would enable him to send Clayton secret information through the mails. This concern about secrecy arose from the fact that Boyle was extremely troubled by piracy of his writings. So much so, in fact, that he wrote a year later, "In the month of May 1688, I thought myself obliged to give notice to the public, that I had, partly by some men's fraud, and partly by mischance, lost so many of my essays and other tracts."[9]

During 1687 Clayton also made the acquaintance, at least by correspondence, of another prominent scientist of the time, Nehemiah Grew (1641–1712). Grew was an alumnus of Cambridge and had received his medical degree from the University of Leyden in 1671. He was at this time quite active in the affairs of the Royal Society. He is best remembered today for *The Anatomy of Plants,* which he published in 1682. In 1698 Grew was granted a patent for Epsom salts, marking the beginning of the commercialization of medical remedies, which had hitherto been kept secret and not sold on the open market.[10] Grew seems to have followed Boyle's custom of sending "Quaeres." He sent twenty-four having to do with the practices, especially medical, of the North American Indians. Clayton was able to answer twenty-two of these questions rather fully, and from these answers we get a very interesting picture of Indian customs, as well as a feeling that Clayton had devoted much time to their study.

The second letter from Clayton to Boyle was written from Wakefield, in Yorkshire. He had just become rector of the ancient Church of All Saints, at Crofton, on July 2, 1687, a post which he held for the next ten years.[11] He seemed to feel

[9] Birch, *Boyle,* I, cxxv.
[10] Dawsons of Pall Mall, *Repository of Medicine and Science and Allied Subjects,* No. 47 (July 1963), p. 2.
[11] Layton, *Discoverer of Gas Lighting,* p. 11.

that he was now hopelessly buried in the sticks and generally
lost to further scientific investigation, and to some extent this
proved to be correct. Crofton has been described in recent
times as "an ancient village with an Anglo-Celtic origin, situated amidst delightful surroundings, although in close prox-
imity to the coal mining district."[12] Clayton did manage to
make a break from Crofton for a short time, for he was in
London during a part of the following winter, carrying on
some research in collaboration with Dr. Allen Moulin
(c.1658–c.1690).

The time of the beginning of Clayton's friendship with
Moulin is in doubt. The two men were close in age and had
mutual friends. Moulin was a very interesting character, and
it is not hard to see why he and Clayton were congenial. On
June 23, 1682, Clayton's old friend from St. Alban days, Dr.
Narcissus Marsh, wrote to Boyle from Trinity College, Dublin,

Sir, the bearer hereof is one Mr. Mullan, batchelor in physic
of this college, who has been successful in several things that
he has undertaken, especially in anatomy, wherein he has good
skill; and had an opportunity the last summer to exercise it on
an occasion, that rarely occurs, namely in dissecting the *elephant,* which was burnt here in *Dublin.*[13]

---

[12] J. S. Fletcher, *A Picturesque History of Yorkshire* (London, 1900), II, 4.
[13] Birch, *Boyle*, VI, 604. Moulin's study of the elephant was published
under the title *An Anatomical Account of the Elephant Accidentally Burnt in
Dublin on Fryday June 17 Sent in a Letter to Sir Will. Petty Fellow of the
Royal Society Together With a Relation of New Anatomical Observations in
the Eyes of Animals: Communicated in Another Letter to the Honourable
R. Boyle, Esq; Fellow of the same Society* by A (llen) M (ullen) Med. of
Trinity College near Dublin (London, 1682). This was his only published
work in addition to his articles in the *Philosophical Transactions* of the
Royal Society of London, according to Theo Hoppen, of University College,
Dublin. Hoppen is preparing a history of the Dublin Philosophical Society.

Moulin[14] spent a year or more in London when he visited Boyle in 1682, possibly as Boyle's assistant, since he mentioned some of their research together.[15] He had received his B.A. from Trinity in 1676 and his M.B. in 1679.[16] He became a member of the Royal Society in July 1683.[17] He returned to Dublin, where he became a charter member of the Dublin Philosophical Society. He gave frequent papers before this society, and they demonstrate the wide range of his research. Subjects included the comparative anatomy of ears and eyes of various animals, water analysis, magnetism, injection of liquids into the veins of dogs, reports of autopsies, and attempts to determine the quantity of blood in man and its rate of circulation.[18] He was a popular physician, with a practice including prominent patients.[19] He had received his M.D. from Trinity College in 1684, becoming a fellow of the Royal College of Physicians in Ireland that same year.[20]

Both Moulin and Clayton were back in London during the early winter of 1687/8, carrying on jointly a series of anatomical studies on birds. Moulin was said to have left Ireland

[14] His name was variously spelled Mullan, Molines, and Mullen, as well as Moulin.

[15] "An Account of an Experiment of the Injection of Mercury into the Blood . . . Experiment at Mr. Boyle's," *Phil. Trans.*, XV (1690), 486.

[16] C. A. Cameron, *History of the Royal College of Surgeons in Ireland* (Dublin, 1916), p. 12.

[17] At a meeting of the Council of the Royal Society of London, July 11, 1683 "Dr. Allen Moulin of Ireland being proposed as a candidate by Dr. Slare, in the name of Mr. Boyle, was approved by the Council." He was elected July 16 (Thomas Birch, *History of the Royal Society of London* [London, 1757], IV, 213–15). Dr. Frederick Slare wrote *Experiments and Observations upon Oriental and Other Bezoar-Stones, which Prove to be of no Use in Physick. Gascoin's Powder, distinctly Examin'd in its Seven Ingredients, Censur'd, and Found Imperfect* (London, 1715).

[18] Birch, *Royal Society*, IV, 273–518 *passim; Phil. Trans.*, XV (1685), illus. facing p. 1107.

[19] Letter of William Molyneux to Thomas Molyneux, spring 1684, in *Dublin University Magazine*, XVIII (1841), 478.

[20] Cameron, *Royal College of Surgeons,* p. 12.

because of a "scandalous love Intrigue, of which he was ashamed."[21] The two men were especially interested in trying to find a correlation between feeding habits and nerve supply to the beaks. They examined such diverse types as parrots, woodcocks, and ducks. Clayton made drawings of some, perhaps all, of their dissections. The results of their studies were presented before the Royal Society by Moulin on February 1. The subsequent publication of the report in the Society's *Transactions,* entitled "Anatomical Observations in the Heads of Fowl Made at Several Times,"[22] makes no mention of Clayton's assistance, but includes an illustration of their dissection of the duck's head, perhaps by Clayton. Moulin doubtless gave him credit verbally at the time, because he certainly was present when the paper was given. The Journal Book of the Society for that date records his observation on another topic: "Mr. Clayton said that Crow-garlick bear on its head a Perfect young plant and may be reckoned among Plantiporous Vegetables."[23] Clayton continued to attend meetings, as a guest of some member, presumably Moulin or Boyle. At the next meeting, a week after Moulin's paper, he took a more active part in the proceedings, for it was recorded that

Mr. Clayton produced a Digesting Engine contrived by himself, being an Improvement of Mr. Papins, being only a Vessel of hammered Copper. He showed likewise his way of Estimating the Degrees of Heat by Letting fall a drop of Water from the same hight as it soaks from a wett Brown paper. He

[21] Walter Harris (ed.), *The Whole Works of Sir James Ware concerning Ireland* (Dublin, 1739–46), III, 206.

[22] XVII (1693), 711–16.

[23] VII (1686–90), 82. The term "plantiporous" does not seem to have survived. It was probably the counterpart of the zoological expression "viviparous," meaning to produce living young (rather than eggs). Viviparous may be used botanically to refer to germination while still attached to the parent plant. Clayton may have been referring to *Allium sativum* L., sometimes called "English garlic," which produces small bulbils in the floral head.

said this Engine of his might be afforded for 10 s., whereas that of Mr. Papin would cost at Least 50 Shillings.[24]

Dr. Papin was no longer in England, as he had left to teach at the University of Marburg. Clayton had met him before his departure and had shown him his model of the Digester.

At the next meeting, on February 15, Clayton participated in a discussion of seed dormancy:

Mr. Clayton gave an Account of Rapeseed lying in the ground 20 years together without Perishing, for that he had been informed that in Huntingdonshire upon turning up of Land which had 20 years before been sown with Rapes, they turned up those seed which had been to[o] deep buried to grow, and thereupon the Rapes were found to come up plentifully in the Ground where none had been known for many years. Mr. Clayton said that seed that have Layn Long in the hold of a ship will not grow in Virginia, wheras those brought over in the Cabbin thrive very well there. It was conceived that the Heat and moysture of the Hold, might cause the seeds to be musty, and thereby spoils there Vegetative Principle.[25]

Clayton made a favorable impression upon the Society, and some of the members asked him to write down his impressions and observations of Virginia. He probably returned to his duties at Wakefield about the middle of February, for his presence at later meetings of the Society is not recorded. On May 16, however,

A Letter from Mr. Clayton was read giving an account of Several Particulars of Naturall History relating to Virginia chiefly as to the Air, promising the same for the Water, Soyl, Birds, Beasts, etc. . . . The Thanks of the Society were ordered to be returned him for these communications and to desire him to proceed at his Leisure.[26]

[24] *Ibid.*, pp. 85–86.   [25] *Ibid.*, p. 87.   [26] *Ibid.*, pp. 113–14.

Dr. Moulin informed Clayton of the Society's wishes, and the second installment of the latter's account, dealing with the Waters, was apparently read in June or July. Clayton also forwarded his copy of the journal of the Batts and Fallam expedition. On August 1, 1688, the Journal Book of the Royal Society recorded:

After the minutes there was produced and read a Large description or Journal of the Voiage of some English and Indians from Virginia in order to Discover the Apalation Mountains. Herein the course they travelled upon, and each days journey, which was thought might be of some use to rectifie the Mapps of America.[27]

On August 17 Clayton resumed his account of Virginia with a description of the soil. Before beginning it, he took time to correct the impression given by the Batts and Fallam journal that they had discovered a tidal river, and he quoted William Byrd as his authority that they must have been mistaken. The account was not read until the following October,[28] and apparently no one wrote to Clayton about it. The Society did, however, elect Clayton to membership, and he formally became a fellow on November 30, 1688.[29]

The promised continuation of Clayton's account was not forthcoming, and no one seems to have pursued the matter until five years later. At that time, Richard Waller, a new secretary of the Society, wrote to Clayton requesting that he continue. He replied on November 24, 1693, that he had discontinued the articles because he had received no word concerning their acceptance or rejection. He was clearly much gratified at being asked to resume, and he proceeded to do so with an account of the birds and promise of continuing

[27] *Ibid.*, p. 138. [28] *Ibid.*, p. 141.
[29] *Record of the Royal Society of London* (4th ed.; London, 1940), p. 526.

with "the Beasts, the Fishes, the Plants the Insects & lastly the present state of the inhabitants."

As a postscript to his letter to Waller, Clayton sent a message to "Mr. Houghton, Esq." concerning the corn market. He had doubtless met John Houghton when he attended meetings of the Royal Society. Houghton edited and wrote articles for two agricultural and trade journals which appeared weekly. They contained letters, articles, and information on crop sales, which he collected from his friends and "correspondents," such as Clayton. John Evelyn, Martin Lister, Thomas Henshaw, and Samuel Dale were among the regular contributors of articles.[30]

On May 22, 1694, Clayton sent to Waller an account of the beasts of Virginia with a long accompanying letter in reply to one from Waller, in which he discussed the melting of iron and gave the account of his Digester's exploding at Sir Thomas Proby's home. If he ever sent Waller the promised accounts of the fishes, plants, insects, and inhabitants of Virginia, no record of them has been found. He did write to Waller at least once more. This was a very hasty note on June 20, 1694, concerning some alum and sulphur which he had found. Except for a receipt for "China Varnish," registered in its book of experiments, this seems to be the end of Clayton's connection with the Royal Society unless two reports credited to "J. C." were his. One was a short article on magnetism and the other on specific gravities of various substances.[31] Since Clayton is known to have had an interest in specific gravities, this article is included here.

[30] *A Collection of Letters for the Improvement of Husbandry and Trade* (London, 1681–83); *Proposal for Improvement of Husbandry and Trade,* which appeared weekly from 1692 to 1703.

[31] "On Magnetism, particularly on the Polarity of a Piece of Iron. By Mr. J. C.," *Phil. Trans.,* XVIII (1694), 257–62; "Observations of the Comparative, Intensive or Specific Gravities of Various Bodies made by Mr. J. C.," *Phil. Trans.,* XVII (1693), 694–95 (see pp. 146–48 below).

Stanley Pargellis considers Clayton to be the author of a manuscript entitled "An Account of the Indians in Virginia (& of some Remarkable / things in that Country / Collected out of some Letters / from A minister in Virginia / Some few things are inserted / Concerning the English there, & the Bucaniers / in some places of America / An Dom / 1689."[32] This seems highly unlikely. Not only is the manner of writing far different from Clayton's rather polished style, but the description of Indian materia medica bears no resemblance to his. If a work by Clayton was the source of this material, it has been very much rewritten by someone else.

It is not surprising that Clayton was not very active as a member of the Royal Society. He seems to have been away from London continuously after his election to membership. The uncertainty concerning the reception of his accounts of Virginia disappointed him, and by the time Waller revived his interest he had become involved in new responsibilities. Wakefield, as he pointed out to Boyle when he went there, was a very small rural community and not quite the place to inspire scientific research. Both Boyle and Moulin died not very long after Clayton left London. Moulin had remained in the city all during the year 1689. In March he had performed "Some Experiments on a Black Shining Sand brought from Virginia, suppos'd to contain Iron . . . ,"[33] which might indicate that he was still in touch with Clayton at that time. Robert Hooke met him several times at Jonathan's Coffee-House in Exchange Alley near Cornhill where fellows of the Royal Society congregated. On December 26 Hooke noted, "Dr. Mullens [sic] tooke his farewell, being to goe for Jamaica tomorrow Morn."[34] Moulin accompanied William O'Brien,

---

[32] *William and Mary Quarterly*, ser. 3, XVI (1959), 228–43. This manuscript is in the Ayer Collection of the Newberry Library, Chicago, Illinois.

[33] *Phil. Trans.*, XVII (1692/3), 624–26.

[34] Portion of Hooke's diary printed in Gunther, *Early Science at Oxford*, X, 153.

Earl of Inchiquin, the newly appointed governor of Jamaica
and hoped to discover some mines to improve his fortune.[35]
Unfortunately, "by putting in at Barbadoes he met with some
Friends who made him drink hard, which threw him into a
calenture of which he died."[36] Boyle died two years later, in
December of 1691.

The date and place of Clayton's marriage are not known,
but in 1694, or perhaps earlier, he married Juliana Edmundson, of Heysham, Lancashire.[37] Juliana was probably the
daughter of Thomas Edmundson, who owned the manor of
Caton.[38] The Claytons' son, Robert, was born August 15,
1695.[39]

MINISTRY IN IRELAND

After ten years as rector of Crofton, Clayton made a rather
drastic move. Perhaps the expense of a family to maintain
caused him to seek a more remunerative post, or perhaps
higher authorities of the Church made the decision for him.
In any event, he was named as rector of St. Michan's, Dublin,
in 1697. Possibly as an omen of things to come, a Mr. Burridge objected bitterly in a letter to the lord justices on
October 15. He complained that there had been an unequal
division of Dean Pooley's living into three parts the previous
May, and that he had received the worst. He suggested that he
be permitted to trade for the "best of the living," which had
been given to Clayton. The lord justices did not consider it

[35] W. B. S. Taylor, *History of the University of Dublin* (London, 1845), p.
374.

[36] Harris, *Sir James Ware,* III, 206.

[37] *Notes and Queries,* ser. 10, XI (1909), 317, quoting from Lodge, "Collections for a Baronage of Ireland," B.M. 23, 710, f. 178.

[38] Francis Gastrell, *Notitia Cestriensis; or, Historic Notices of the Diocese
of Chester,* ed. F. R. Raines (Chetham Society, *Remains, Historical &
Literary* . . . , Vol. XXII [Manchester, 1850]), p. 439.

[39] G. D. Burtchaell and T. U. Sadleir, *Alumni Dublinenses* (Dublin, 1936).

proper to effect any changes, but recommended that Mr. Burridge be given an additional preferment.[1] Clayton moved his family to Ireland and became rector of St. Michan's April 29, 1698.[2]

St. Michan's had been built by the Danes in the eleventh century. From this period only the tower remained. In 1686 the church had been repaired and renovated. When Clayton arrived, it was called the "new St. Michans." Layton says,

A reference to the list of seatholders gives the impression that the congregation to which the new incumbent was called to minister included a large proportion of the aristocracy and culture of the Irish capital. Seats were allotted to the Archbishop of Armagh, the Earl of Drogheda, the Lord Chancellor, the Lord Chief Justice, Lord Massereene, and many baronets, knights, and officers of the crown.[3]

Neither its age nor its fashionable congregation was what made St. Michan's so well known. It was the curious reputation of its vaults. By some special quirk of excessive dryness, the bodies had been preserved for many centuries in a mummified state. The "Silent Traveller," Chiang Yee, gave a vivid account of his visit there in the nineteen-fifties.[4]

The Ireland to which the Claytons came was still suffering from the upheaval less than ten years before when Tyrconnel had seized the country for James II. The Roman Catholics had destroyed the churches and imprisoned the clergy, some of whom barely escaped with their lives. The Treaty of Limerick, October 3, 1691, marked the end of Ireland's short period of independence. In spite of the freedom of religion

[1] Great Britain, *State Papers, Domestic, 1697*, ed. W. J. Hardy (London, 1927), p. 42.

[2] Layton, *Discoverer of Gas Lighting*, p. 25.

[3] *Ibid.*, p. 26.

[4] Chiang Yee, *The Silent Traveller in Dublin* (New York, 1953), pp. 42–43.

guaranteed under the treaty, many anti-Catholic laws were passed in the next few years. They were not engendered solely by a wish for reprisal, but rather from a very real fear of the excesses which had been so recently committed by the Roman Catholics. The latter were barred from public office and from practicing law; they were not allowed to carry weapons nor to own a horse worth more than five pounds. They were not permitted to attend the university at home or to study abroad. They not only paid tithes to the Church of England but were subject to the demands of their own priests. They were forbidden to send money overseas to Rome or to use it at home to train priests.[5] Many of their estates had been confiscated, and of those men who had not been killed during the fighting, many fled to France. A contemporary, Sir Richard Coxe, wrote that "those who are left are destitute of horses, arms, money, capacity, and courage. Five out of six of the Irish are insignificant slaves, fit for nothing but to hew wood and draw water."[6]

Because of all the destruction, poverty was prevalent for many years afterward. Guy Meigs wrote:

The Streets of the City of *Dublin,* for several Years past, . . . [have] swarm'd with Crouds of miserable Objects, whose Wants and Infirmities had been shamefully exposed to publick View, to the Reproach of human Nature, and the Dishonour of Religion, through the want of a due Provision for the Reception and Imployment of Beggars and other Poor of the City Parishes.[7]

The mayor and the city fathers bought land for a workhouse in

---

[5] T. J. Johnston, J. L. Robinson, and R. W. Jackson, *A History of the Church of Ireland* (Dublin, 1953), pp. 217–18.

[6] R. B. O'Brien (ed.), *Two Centuries of Irish History, 1691–1870* (London, 1907), p. 16.

[7] *The Present State of Great Britain and Ireland* (London, 1718), part III, p. 48.

1703, and the Duchess of Ormonde, wife of the Lord Lieutenant, contributed. Doubtless impressed by such scenes, Clayton founded two charity schools in St. Michan's churchyard, to which he left a legacy in his will.[8] It is also likely that he continued to practice medicine among those unable to afford the services of a physician.

In spite of the grinding poverty, the gentry and the clergy managed to live a comfortable and often luxurious life. It must be remembered that the shocking contrast between the two modes of living was the accepted standard for the seventeenth and eighteenth centuries. Dublin was a bustling, gay, and amusing city. Trinity College satisfied intellectual curiosity, the streets were lined with bookstalls, and for those who were unable to buy there was Bishop Marsh's Library, the first public library of the city. The incomparable Irish theater was always popular. Even the English could not long preserve their usual reserve in the hospitable social climate.[9] It was a tremendous change for Clayton from the quiet isolation of Wakefield. Unfortunately the Dublin Philosophical Society, which Clayton's old teacher, Narcissus Marsh, and his friends had established when he was provost of Trinity, no longer existed. It had been suspended during the short reign of James II. There was a movement to revive it in 1693 and again after Clayton went to Ireland, in 1707. At that time the meetings were only resumed for a year and Clayton was not a member.[10]

Resentment was stirred against the Established Church by the fact that, almost without exception, the top appointments

---

[8] Memoir of Bishop Robert Clayton, manuscript copy by Robert Chapman, with notes and addenda, Archives of Trinity College, Dublin.

[9] A vivid picture of Irish life at this time is given in Constantia Maxwell, *Country and Town Life in Ireland under the Georges* (London, 1940).

[10] Constantia Maxwell, *A History of Trinity College, Dublin, 1591–1892* (Dublin, 1946), p. 79.

went to Englishmen.[11]   Many of them enjoyed their whole tenure *in absentia*.   John Hacket never set foot in Ireland during the twenty years in which he was Bishop of Down.[12] The salaries allowed the ministers were extremely miserly, some as little as five pounds a year.   Thus it was that the rectors often held four to seven livings simultaneously and vied for the Dublin appointments.   In the capital they were much more assured of preferment than when forgotten in some country town.[13]

Traditionally the rector of St. Michan's held a prebendal stall in ancient Christ Church Cathedral, the foundations of which had been laid by the Danish prince of Dublin in 1038.[14] Clayton was formally installed as prebendary on May 5, 1698.[15] This office soon plunged him into the midst of the controversy which raged for some years between the dean of the Cathedral (William Moreton),[16] on the one hand, and the Archbishop of

[11] Meigs, *Present State,* part III, p. 57.   There were four archbishops and nineteen bishops.   William King (1650–1729), Archbishop of Dublin, was one of the very few natives who held such high office.

[12] W. E. H. Lecky, *A History of Ireland in the Eighteenth Century* (London, 1912) I, 205–6.   Such men often sold their benefices or gave them to relatives. Not only did the Church suffer resentment because of this, but it was operating under great financial difficulties.   Many of the churches which had been destroyed by the Roman Catholics were being rebuilt during the reign of Queen Anne, which made a drain on Church finances.

[13] Maxwell, *Country and Town Life in Ireland,* p. 322.

[14] R. C. Hoare, *Journal of a Tour in Ireland* (London, 1807), p. 13.

[15] Layton, *Discoverer of Gas Lighting,* pp. 25–26.

[16] Moreton (1641–1715) was Bishop of Kildare.   He was a native of Chester and an Oxford graduate.   He had come to Ireland as chaplain to James, Duke of Ormonde, who was Lord Lieutenant, and had been appointed dean of the Cathedral, becoming bishop in 1682.   At the time of James II, he was forced to leave, but returned upon William III's ascension to the throne. When Dopping, the Bishop of Meath, had stated in a sermon that the freedom of religion clause in the Treaty of Limerick should not be kept because the Irish were such a "perfidious people," Moreton had publicly taken the opposite viewpoint.   William III removed Dopping from the Privy Council, giving Moreton his seat (O'Brien, *Irish History,* pp. 8–9).

Dublin (William King), on the other.[17] Archbishop King claimed jurisdiction over the powerful Cathedral, with its twenty-seven associated churches. A legal suit was initiated in 1704, which lasted twenty years.[18] As early as 1703 Clayton was sent to England on this business, to which there is a reference in a letter of Bishop Compton to William King, October 20:

I understood lately that there was an appeal come over from Ireland wherein your Grace was concerned, & that your humble servant was named one of yr Delegates. As I was enquiring about the business, one told me that it was Mr. Clayton that brought over the Appeal, that if I thought it might be any service to Your Grace to avoid the noise of contests among ourselves, he would safely show me how I might persuade Mr. Clayton to submit to an amicable Reference. Your Grace is best judge of what is fit to be done. If you approve of the proposition, I will do my best to comply with your commands; or if I am under a mistake most heartily I beg your pardon & remain with great respects

My Lord
Your graces most obedient
Humble Servant   H:London[19]

It was probably on this visit that Clayton examined the records of old cases of a similar nature in the Tower of London. He was successful in his search for precedents and made copies of several which he included in his petition to the Duke of Ormonde on the behalf of the dean and chapter of the Cathedral sometime in 1705.

Upon his return to Ireland, Clayton continued to work for Moreton, who wrote to Ormonde on August 5, 1704, relative to the ecclesiastical dispute. The Bishop of Kildare stated

[17] Johnston, Robinson, and Jackson, *History of the Church,* p. 216.
[18] *Ibid.*
[19] Archives of Trinity College, Dublin.

that he was threatened by King with suspension from his dean's office and excommunication. He was sending Mr. Clayton and Mr. Justice Upton to present his case.[20] Clayton's activities did not pass unnoticed. The man who acted as receiver of the archbishop's rents wrote to Robert King in January 1704/5: "I hope . . . that no such snarling creature as Mr. Clayton will be able to blemish his character tho' I don't find that all his malice has been able to make an impression here."[21] The quarrel was not confined to the bounds of the Church, but had political implications as well. Sir Thomas Southwell petitioned Ormonde on December 19, 1704:

Asking his Grace to intimate his pleasure to the Lords Justices to make the writer Lt. of the county Limerick, that by the credit of it he may be the better able to oppose the interest that the Speaker and Mr. Clayton are now making there to procure a knight of the shire to be chosen in the room of the deceased, Mr. Oliver.[22]

In a judgment worthy of Solomon himself Ormonde persuaded Queen Anne to appoint Moreton Bishop of Meath, and his own chaplain, Webore Ellis, to the bishopric of Kildare and the deanery, thus solving some of the personal ill feeling.[23] Moreton was keenly appreciative of all the work that Clayton had done for him and wrote to Ormonde on August 28, 1705:

Your Grace's of the 21st I received last night, and with it an inexpressible satisfaction to find your Grace so immovable and steady to one of the oldest servants of your family. . . . As for

[20] Great Britain, Historical Manuscripts Commission, *Calendar of the Manuscripts of the Marquess of Ormonde, K. P., Preserved at Kilkenny Castle*, new ser. (London, 1900–20) , VIII, 105.

[21] Charles King (ed.) , *A Great Archbishop of Dublin, William King, D.D., 1650–1729* (London, 1906) , p. 107.

[22] H.M.C., *Ormonde*, VIII, 125–26.

[23] Archbishop Marsh to Ormonde, September 5, 1705, *ibid.*, pp. 181–82.

my church, which I am now going to leave, it hath many royal-
ties, both in its foundation and superstructure, as any church
hath or need to have; for by its charter it appears to be a peculiar of the Crown's own making, as it was formerly of the Pope's,
and it hath privileges which can never be in danger whilst your
Grace continues the patron of it, which makes me hope that my
successor, in case the Archbishop will not let fall his suit,
will take up the gauntlet which I lay down, the cause I plead
for being a most righteous cause I am sure, and of considerable
consequence and moment to the prerogative of the Crown. I
must likewise presume to hope that the gentleman who has
borne the burthen and the heat of the day, I mean Dr. Clayton,
will have a Share of your Grace's favour, he being the principal
manager of this cause and a very fortunate assistant of, my
Lord, etc.[24]

There seems to be no further mention of Clayton in this
regard, although as late as 1724 William King described his
old enemies at Christ Church Cathedral in uncomplimentary
terms: "They live in opposition to all mankind . . .
squander away their economy, have turned their Chapter-
house into a toy-shop, their vaults into wine-cellars & allowed a
room in the body of their church, formerly for a grand jury
room, & now for a robe-room for the judges."[25]

In addition to his stall at the Cathedral, Clayton was appointed Precentor of Waterford in 1699 and remained in this
position until installed as the first Canon of Kildare on July 19,
1705.[26] The church had been destroyed during the civil war
and was never rebuilt.

He returned to London in the late fall of 1705, since
Rawlinson records a sermon "Christ crucified the power of
God and the mystery of God a sermon preached at St. Mar-

[24] *Ibid.*, pp. 179–80.
[25] Quoted in Johnston, Robinson, and Jackson, *History of the Church*,
p. 216.
[26] Layton, *Discoverer of Gas Lighting*, p. 28.

garetts Westminster, Novemb. 11, 1705, published at the request of severall of the hearers – Lond. 1706 – 4to on Corinth.
22 v. 23 24."[27]   Another of his sermons had been published in
1700: *A Sermon preach'd at St. Michan's Church in Dublin . . . upon receiving into the Communion of the Church
of England, the Hon*[ble] *Sir Terence Mac-Mahon . . . and
Christopher Dunn, converts from the Church of Rome.
Wherein is an account also of a late controversy betwixt the
Author and some Romanists.*[28]   The Roman Catholics objected to some of his remarks and made some of their own, to
which Clayton replied in a *Defense of a sermon,* 1701, and the
following year in *Reply to Father Nary's Answer.*   His only
other publication was *Dean Clayton's Letter to one of the
Common Council of the City of Dublin,* 1713.[29]

On December 7, 1708, Clayton was elected Dean of Kildare,
and Layton believes that the degree of doctor of divinity was
conferred on him at that time.[30]   However, Moreton was
calling Clayton "Dr." in 1705 (see quotation on p. liii).
Although there are numerous references to Clayton's holding
such a degree, there is no record that it was given by his own
university, nor was it conferred by the University of Dublin.

Age and the many duties of church and family seem to have
precluded many outside activities, and the events of the remainder of Clayton's life can only be presumed in relation to
his children.   William Narcissus Clayton was born in 1699
and christened on May 8.[31]   He was named for Narcissus

---

[27] MSS Rawlinson, J. 4. 3, Bodleian Library, Oxford University.

[28] B.M. 4473.g.1 (9); there is also a copy in the Cashel Collection, Library
of The Representative Body of the Church of Ireland, Dublin.

[29] Copies of these are in the Trinity College Library, Dublin.   For this, and
other information, we are very much indebted to Mr. William O'Sullivan,
archivist.   The Royal Irish Academy has a copy of the last item, and doubtless
there are many others elsewhere.

[30] Layton, *Discoverer of Gas Lighting,* p. 28.

[31] *Ibid.,* p. 26.

Marsh, then Archbishop of Armagh, and a parishioner of St. Michan. William died in childhood, and the Clayton family then consisted of the parents, Robert, and three daughters, Eleanor, Anne, and Elizabeth.[32] Although Robert was the only son, he was one of whom the Claytons could be justly proud. He attended Westminster school, and much of the credit for his excellent record was due to his tutors, a Mr. Walmsley and Zachary Pearce, later Bishop of Bangor and Rochester. The year after his father was made dean, Robert matriculated at Trinity College on June 25 at the age of fifteen. In 1714 he received his degree, simultaneously becoming a fellow.[33] In the succeeding 250 years this has been achieved only once.[34]

The next summer Clayton's older brother, William, died after a long and successful career as merchant and member of Parliament. Since he left five daughters but no son, the Fulwood estates passed to John Clayton.[35] The dean may already have been comfortably situated because of a well-to-do wife, but certainly William's death ensured a fairly luxurious scale of living, and he has been referred to as "wealthy." Perhaps this affluence was the reason that young Robert toured the Continent about this time. It may also have been the reason for Clayton's marital advice to his son. It was reported that Robert had

often been heard to relate the pains his father took to engage him to seek after a wife with a plentiful dowry. The old gentleman, in order to obtain his son's compliance, would argue, that a Lady's bestowing upon him a large fortune, was

[32] Abstracts from Irish Wills, made by Sir William Betham, manuscript volume in the library of the Society of Genealogists, Dublin.

[33] Burtchaell and Sadleir, *Alumni Dublinenses.*

[34] Chapman, "Bishop Clayton."

[35] His will, dated February 12, 1713, is in the Lancashire Record Office at Preston.

the surest testimony she could exhibit of her sincere & un-feigned affection. But our Doctor, whose mind was far raised above pecuniary considerations, was resolved to follow the dictates of his own heart.[36]

In 1717 Robert took his M.A. and the next year his L.L.B., the degree of L.L.D. being conferred in 1722. On May 2, 1720, Mrs. Clayton had died. Her funeral took place at St. Michan's Church.

In the early summer of 1725 a very fine organ was installed at St. Michan's, where it can still be admired for its intricately carved case.[37] In September, Clayton wrote a letter to the archbishop, suggesting a change in afternoon "lecturers" at St. Michan's. Some of the parishioners were "dissatisfied with Mr. Needham's preaching." This appears to be his last sur-viving letter, for he died on September 23, 1725. Layton quotes from a manuscript volume in the British Museum, entitled "Funeral Entries of Ireland": "The Rev.ᵈ Dean Clayton died at his house in Church Street and was Interᵈ in St. Michan's Church, Dublin, Sept 26ᵗʰ, 1725, wᵗʰ Funerall Solemnities – Where Mr. Crossly by falling into a Celler got his Death – died 8ʰᵉʳ 1ˢᵗ 1725."[38]

Clayton's will, written two years earlier, was probated Sep-tember 26, 1725, but has since been destroyed. Robert did not consider that his father had made sufficient provision in the will for his sisters. "On the decease of his father . . . Mr. Clayton got possession of a large fortune; he then generously gave to each of his three sisters double the portion left them by their father's will."[39] Eleanor, who married John Bayley of

---

[36] Chapman, "Bishop Clayton," p. 97.

[37] Layton, *Discoverer of Gas Lighting*, p. 31.

[38] *Ibid.*, pp. 31–32.

[39] W. B. S. Taylor, *History of the University of Dublin* (London, 1845), p. 407.

Gouran, County Kilkenny, had two sons, Robert and Samuel. Elizabeth married a Mr. Brown, and Anne, William Reeves of Upper Court, County Kilkenny.[40] Dean Clayton's advice was not wasted upon Robert, for he resigned as senior fellow at Trinity College in order to marry Catherine, daughter of Lord Chief Baron Donnellan.[41] His clerical career was quite as distinguished as his scholarly one had been and was marked by a judicious courting of the favors of his cousin's wife, Lady Sundon, lady in waiting to the queen.[42] He became Bishop of Killala and Anchonry, 1729–30, of Cork and Ross, 1735, and Clogher, 1745. The degree of doctor of divinity was conferred upon him by the University of Dublin in 1730.[43] He was a prolific writer; John Nichols credits him with twelve publications.[44] His works were primarily theological and, as a result of the inquiring mind inherited from his father, they often landed him in contentions with the clergy.[45]

[40] *Notes and Queries,* ser. 10, XI (1909), 317.

[41] Lord Donnellan was president of the Court of Exchequer.

[42] "Mrs. Clayton, afterwards Lady Sundon . . . as Bedchamber Woman to Queen Caroline . . . practically controlled the patronage of the Court" (S. J. Reid, *John and Sarah, Duke and Duchess of Marlborough, 1660–1744* [London, 1914], p. 441). Many of Bishop Clayton's letters are among Lady Sundon's papers in the British Museum.

[43] *D.N.B.*

[44] John Nichols, *Literary Anecdotes of the Eighteenth Century* (London, 1812–16), II, 241–44.

[45] Two quotations give an interesting picture of the life led by Dean Clayton's son and his wife. The first was written by Mrs. Delaney to her sister, Anne Granville, on August 13, 1742:

"We had excellent sport at the fair; I gave you an account of the method that was to be observed, the games and the prizes. About eleven o'clock Mrs. Clayton, well attended, in her coach drawn by six flouncing Flanders mares, went on the strand, three heats the first race. The second gave us much more sport, five horses put in, the last horse to win, and every man rode his neighbour's horse without saddle, whip, or spur. Such hollowing, kicking of legs, sprawling of arms, *could not* be seen *without laughing immoderately;* in the afternoon chairs were placed before the house, where we all took our places in

Just before Christmas of 1740, the bishop wrote to his friend, the Earl of Egmont, sending him copies of two of his father's papers which he had found. These were notes on his experiments with the "Spirit of Coals" and the "Nitrous Particles of the Air." They were read before the Royal Society of London a month later. Several months afterward Clayton's "Elasticity of the Air" was read. All three were published in the Society's *Transactions,* as were also some of the bishop's own writings. As a result, Dean Clayton's papers were indexed under his son's name. Because they were published long after the dean's death, they have often been ascribed to his distant cousin and namesake, the Virginia botanist.

The bishop, like his father before him, became a fellow of the Royal Society of London, having been proposed by the Earl of Egmont on January 12, 1743/4.[46] A bust of Robert Clayton, by Simon Vierpyl, is in the Long Room of the Trinity College Library, and his portrait is in the Palace at Cork.

---

great state, all Attired in our best apparel, it being Mrs. Clayton's birthday; then dancing, singing, grinning, accompanied with an excellent bagpipe, the whole concluded with a ball, bonfire, and illuminations; pray does *your Bishop* promote such entertainments at Gloster as ours does at Killala?" (The Rt. Hon. Lady Llanover [ed.], *The Autobiographies and Correspondence of Mary Granville, Mrs. Delaney* [London, 1861], I, 373).

The second quotation is taken from a letter written to Thomas Southern by John, fifth Earl of Orrery, in 1742:

"We are not entirely void of Elegance at Corke. We have a Bishop, who, as He has travel'd beyond the Alps, has brought home with him, to the amazement of our mercantile Fraternity, the Arts and Sciences that are the Ornament of Italy and the Admiration of the European World. He eats, drinks, and sleeps in Taste. He has pictures by Carlo, Music by Corelli, Castles in the Air by Vitruvius; and on High-Days and Holidays We have the Honour of Catching Cold at a Venetian door. To Crown All, he is nearly allied to Lady Sundon . . . Under the Reign of Dr. Clayton We sing Catches, read *Pastor Fido,* and talk of Love. Thus if One Road does not lead to Paradise, we try another" (Emily, Countess of Cork and Orrery [ed.], *The Orrery Papers* [London, 1903], I, 206).

[46] Journal Book of the Royal Society, XVIII (1742–45), 184.

Mention is also made of a portrait done at Armagh in 1745, but no likeness of his father seems to have survived.[47]

Because he had no children, the bishop willed the Lancashire estates to his nearest male relative, Richard Clayton, grandson of his father's brother, Richard, and Chief Justice of Common Pleas. The bulk of his estate went to his niece, who had married Dr. Barnard, Dean of Derry, later Bishop of Killala and Bishop of Limerick. In order not to revive old arguments and controversy, Dr. Barnard suppressed all the papers and manuscripts inherited by his wife.[48] Whether or not these were destroyed is not indicated, but they certainly included some of Dean Clayton's papers as well as those of his son.

CLAYTON, THE SCIENTIST

Like many others of his day Clayton was financially able to be a part-time scientist only. Few full-time careers open to scientists would support them. Clayton might have devoted his full time to medicine, and it seems likely that he may have considered this, since he certainly acquired a considerable medical training. Blanton, the authority on the practice of medicine in colonial Virginia, considered that he "was apparently practising medicine on a parity with regular physicians."[1] This was probably largely confined to times when other doctors were not available. He elected to make the Church his occupation, and scientific pursuits an avocation. His scientific contributions must be evaluated with this in mind. He was fortunate in receiving an excellent education, and he was thus able to appreciate the importance of his observations. Whether by instinct or by training, he ap-

[47] According to Mr. O'Sullivan, Trinity College, Dublin.
[48] Chapman, "Bishop Clayton," p. 25.
[1] W. B. Blanton, *Medicine in Virginia in the Seventeenth Century* (Richmond, 1930), p. 142.

proached every new situation with an open but an inquiring
mind.   Oxford indoctrinated him thoroughly in the importance of detailed observations and the value of experiments in
providing answers to well-formulated questions.   He was
something of a philosopher, as most great scientists have been,
interested in very broad questions as well as in detailed ones.

By present-day standards Clayton's scientific interests were
astonishingly varied.   This was fairly normal in his time,
when an interest in natural history was still scientifically
respectable and one did not need to embrace a specialty.   This
was also accentuated in Clayton's case by the fact that much of
his limited scientific writing was devoted to an account of his
observations of a recently settled and still little-known land.
He had gone to Virginia with a sound scientific training and
with the intention of learning as much as possible about its
many curiosities.   It would be expected that his observations
would cover a wide range of subjects.   Judgment of the extent
and quality of his comments must take into account the fact
that they were made several years after his return to England.
In spite of these reservations, it is surprising to find that his
accounts of Virginia contain material still of interest to special-
ists in a number of scientific fields.   Thus his description of a
disease of tobacco is cited by a plant pathologist as the earliest
recorded account of something that is still a problem.[2]
Ornithologists are impressed by the number of birds which
they can identify from his descriptions and consider his accounts outstanding for that time.[3]   His comments on soil are
still pertinent and are said to be "the earliest American records

[2] See p. 65, n. 41.
[3] See p. 93, n. 2, and also E. G. Allen, "The History of American
Ornithology before Audubon," *Trans. of the Amer. Phil. Soc.*, new ser.,
XLI (1951), 459–61.

of soil science."[4] A current study of early American geology cites his comments on waters and on fossils.[5] There is much of interest for the botanist, despite the fact that Clayton apparently never wrote the projected account of plants. Ethnologists enjoy his descriptions of Indian customs, as should anyone with an interest in pharmacognosy or materia medica.[6]

Clayton's scientific activities in England, as opposed to his observations in Virginia, may be a better measure of his true interests, but here also we find that they are varied. All of them might be referred to broadly as medical research, but they included, among other things, anatomy, physiology, chemistry, and physics. He worked with Dr. Moulin in dissecting the nerves of birds, a rather difficult anatomical chore, and he referred to a number of other anatomical studies. He mentioned many experiments involving the injection of various substances into the blood stream of dogs and subsequent autopsies to determine the cause of death. These he related to the use of similar substances in human medical treatment and possible ill effects on patients. He made determinations of the specific gravities of urines and related them to medical diagnosis. He was very much interested in the chemical composition and physical behavior of air and water, and he designed experimental apparatus for studying their behavior in relation to heat and pressure.

The ability to design and construct experimental apparatus is always an asset to a scientist, but it was almost a necessity in Clayton's time, when comparatively little could be purchased.

[4] C. A. Browne, "Reverend Dr. John Clayton and His Early Map of Jamestown, Virginia," *William and Mary Quarterly,* ser. 2, XIX (1939), 1–2.

[5] G. W. White, "Early American Geology," *Scientific Monthly,* LXXVI (March 1953), 137–38.

[6] B. G. Hoffman, "John Clayton's 1687 Account of the Medicinal Practices of the Virginia Indians," *Ethnohistory,* XI (Winter, 1964), 1–40.

He seems to have been especially adept at this. He made a number of improved models of Papin's Digester and demonstrated one of them to the Royal Society. He designed special glasses for his specific gravity studies and had these blown for him.

Clayton's most important scientific discovery was probably his determination that coal can be distilled, with the formation of coal tars and the release of an inflammable gas capable of being stored and controlled. Had he proceeded to put this to the practical use which now seems obvious, he would have been widely heralded as a scientist in his own day. As has so often happened in the history of science, however, he reported his experiments with evident excitement, but failed to suggest their practical application. As a result, a century elapsed before a house was lighted by coal gas, and two and a half centuries passed before Layton gave him official credit as the discoverer of gas lighting. This might suggest that Clayton was strictly a theorist, lacking in practical sense. This was by no means the case, and he did not wish to be so considered. He liked to demonstrate the practical nature of his ideas, and he used such expressions as "for this I have something more than bare conjecture," and "this is no fond projection." In his studies of plants and Indian remedies he was intensely interested in practical medicinal uses. His studies of urines were to aid in diagnosis. He liked to apply scientific principles to agricultural practices and was extremely irritated when he could not convince farmers that his suggestions were practical. The speaking trumpet which he devised was used to save the leaking ship at his suggestion.

One of Clayton's assets as a scientist was a gift for colorful writing. His scientific observations were reported with an admirable use of language which makes them a pleasure to read. His use of old expressions presented a bit of a problem to his editors. When seeking an explanation for the expression "like Barme on an Ale fat," they turned to the ever-helpful *Oxford English Dictionary*. Here they not only found the meaning, but also an example quoted from Clayton. This experience occurred four times.

Speculation concerning what Clayton might have accomplished as a scientist under other circumstances is pointless. On a basis of what he did do, we must recognize that the parson was a scientist of imagination, ability, and versatility.

SCIENTIFIC WRITINGS OF
THE REVEREND JOHN CLAYTON
AND RELATED PAPERS

The attempt has been made to transcribe Clayton's writings which are available in the original manuscripts with a minimum of change. Certain concessions to practical demands have been necessary. These include rendition of all thorns as "th," expanding the symbols used for double letters and for "er" and "or," and bringing all superscript letters down, with the exception of "l" in the title of colonel, which has been omitted. Otherwise spelling, abbreviations, capitalization, and punctuation have been transcribed as the editors interpret them, in spite of many inconsistencies. Parenthetic statements by Clayton have been rendered in angle brackets. Those writings which no longer exist in manuscript have been reproduced exactly as previously published.

VIRGINIA: "WHERE PLENTY MAKES POVERTY, IGNORANCE INGENUITY, & COVETEOUSNESSE CAUSES HOSPITALITY"

Letter to a Doctor of Physik[1]

James Citty[2]
Ap: the 24th [16]84

Honour'd Doctor

I am now in Virginy in good health god be prais'd   we had a tedious long voiage twelve weekes twixt land & land   as to noveltys I can give you no account   Tis the multitude distract me & the shortnesse of my time will not permit   Tis now our Great Assembly & on Sunday by a peculiar order from the Governer & Councell I am to preach so that somthing peculiar is expected & I must mind my hits to preserve that blooming repute I have got.   I have had the happinesse to be cried up farr beyond my deserts   the people are peculiarly obligeing, quick & subtile.   The land firtile comodious pleasant & health-

---

[1] Printed from B.M., Sloane MSS 1008, f. 334–35. This letter is among other papers of Edmund Borlase and has been assumed by some to have been written to him, although it does not say so. It seems more probable that it was written to the Dr. Williamson mentioned. It was printed in the *William and Mary Quarterly*, ser. 2, I (1921), 114–15, where it differs somewhat from the original manuscript in punctuation, spelling, and a few words. Dr. Borlase, historian as well as physician, was the son of Sir John Borlase, Lord Justice of Ireland. Educated in Dublin, he received his M.D. in Leyden in 1650. A note on one of his letters (B.M., Sloane MSS 1008, f. 49) says that he died "1682?" but the D.N.B. considers this questionable.

[2] James City Parish is probably intended, rather than Jamestown.

full saveing only the Distemper of the Colick[3] that is predominant & has miserable sad effects   it begins wth violent gripes[4]
wch declineing takes away the use of limbs   their fingers stand
stifly bent   the hands of some hang as if they were loose at the
wrists from the arms, they are scelatons so meager & leane that
a consumption might seeme a fatning to them, cruelly are they
distracted wth a flatus[5] & at length those that seemeingly
recover are oft troubled wth a sort of a gout   pray send me yr
opinion wt course might be most proper for I dread it myselfe
And direct me wt Authors have writ concerning it   I would
now give you a further account of the Country but that then
my thoughts might be as wild as the place   that is all one
continued wood but take this in short   its a place where plenty
makes poverty, Ignorance ingenuity, & coveteousnesse causes
hospitality   that is thus   evry one covets so mch & there is such
vast extent of land that they spread so far they cannot manage
well a hundred pt of wt they have   evry one can live at ease &
therefore they scorne & hate to worke to advantage themselves
so are poor wth abundance   They have few Schollars so that
evry one studys to be halfe Physitian   halfe Lawyer & with a
naturall accutenesse would amuse thee for want of bookes they
read men the more   Then for the third thing Ordinarys   ie
our Inns   are extreame expensive   wherefore with a comon
impudence they'le goe to a mans house for diet & lodgeings tho
they have no acquaintance at all rather than be at the expence
to lie at an Inn & being grown into rank custom it makes them
seem liberall   when the trouble of our Assembly [is over a] full

[3] Blanton (*Medicine in Virginia in the Seventeenth Century,* p. 66) says
that this sounds like lead colic, probably from lead containers for potables.
There had been an epidemic in France in 1572, and in the eighteenth century
Devonshire colic was caused by the use of leaden vats and cider presses.
It sometimes resulted from water collected from leaden roofs and gutters.
[4] Spasmodic pain in the intestines.
[5] Gas generated in the stomach or bowels.

account of affairs I shall then send but this busie time happen-
ing so imediately af[te]r my comeing here makes both my
hands full   yet I was resolvd to force me to scraul a line or two
to him I so mch respect & shall ever honour the Dear Dr
Williamson[6] whom I shall evr desire to oblige & serve as a

Faithfull friend

J Clayton

Pray send me an account of all new bookes Experimts or other
things happen   Amongst yr patients you may perhaps meet
with some one has a peculiar knack at makeing cheese   a very
good Chesshire cheese[7] might oblige & should not be wth out a
returne   wt ever you would send to me   letter or so forth
direct it for me at James Citty Virginy   Sending it to Mr Perry
& Lane Merchants in London

My humble respects & service to that honest dear rogue H.
Harper & his brothers[8] as also to the Apothecarys &c our
friends

[6] Probably Dr. Edward Williamson, physician and widely known anti-
quarian of Chester. G. L. Fenwick (*A History of the Ancient City of Chester*
[Chester, Eng., 1896], p. 424) says that four generations of one family, all
named Randle Holme, collected information on Chester's history: "These
were condensed by Dr. Williamson into one thick quarto volume called
'Villare Cestrense,' arranged in Hundreds and Parishes.   Bishop Gastrell
afterwards abridged and published this as 'Notitia Cestrensis.' " Ormerod
called Williamson "one of the most laborious and certainly the most intelligent of the Cheshire collectors. . . . It is only well merited praise of
this book to say, that its contents are more useful and important to an
investigator of Cheshire antiquities, than all which the successive generations
of the Randle Holmes have treasured up in three hundred volumes" (George
Ormerod, *The History of the County Palatine and City of Chester*, [rev. and
ed.] Thomas Helsby [London, 1882], II, 752).   The reference to apothecaries
in the postscript of this letter may contain an explanation of what Clayton
had been doing just prior to going to Virginia: he might have been a
medical intern at Chester under Dr. Williamson.

[7] At least twenty ships annually carried Cheshire and Lancashire cheeses
to London (Henry Fishwick, *History of Lancashire* [London, 1894], p. 162).

[8] H. Harper remains unidentified.

II

"THE RELATION OF STRANGE ACCIDENT"

Letter to Mr. Robert Boyle[1]

Virginia, James-City, June 23, 1684

Honoured and worthy Sir,

In England having perused, among the rest of your admirable treatises, that ingenious discourse of the Noctiluca,[2] wherein, as I remember, you gave an account of several nocturnal irradiations; having therefore met with the relation of strange accident in that nature, from very good hands, I presumed this might not prove unwelcome; for the fuller confirmation of which, I have inclosed the very paper colonel Diggs[3] gave me thereof, under his own hand and name, to attest the truth; the same being likewise asserted to me by Madam Diggs his lady, sister to the said Susanna Sewall, daughter to the Lord Baltimore,[4] lately gone for England, who I suppose may give you fuller satisfaction of such particulars as you may be desirous to

---

[1] Reprinted from *The Works of the Honourable Robert Boyle,* ed. Henry Miles (London, 1772), VI, 659–60. Robert Boyle (1627–91), chemist and physicist.

[2] *Aerial Noctiluca* (London, 1680), or *Icy Noctiluca* (London, 1680).

[3] William Digges, member of the Maryland Council and secretary in 1689. For a fuller account of his career, see Raphael Semmes, *Captains and Mariners of Early Maryland* (Baltimore, 1937).

[4] Charles Calvert (1637–1713), third Lord Baltimore, the proprietor of Maryland. His second wife was Jane Sewall, widow of Secretary Henry Sewall (H. C. Forman, *Jamestown and St. Mary's* [Baltimore, 1938], pp. 235–36).

be informed of. I cannot but admire the strangeness of such a complicated spirit of a volatile salt and exalted oil,[5] as I deem it to be, from its crepitation[6] and shining flame: how it should transpire through the pores, and not be inflamed by the joint motion and heat of the body, and afterwards so suddenly to be actuated into sparks by the shaking or brushing of her coats, raises much my wonder.

Another thing I am confident your honour would be much pleased at the sight of, a fly we have here, called the firefly, about the bigness of the cantharides;[7] its body of a dark colour, the tail of it a deep yellow by day, which by night shines brighter than the glow-worm; which bright shining ebbs and flows, as if the fly breathed with a shining spirit. I pulled the tail of the fly in several pieces, and every part thereof would shine for several hours after, and cast a light round it. Be pleased favourably to interpret this fond impertinency of a stranger.[8] All your works have to the world evidenced your goodness, which has encouraged the presumption, and it is that which bids me hope its pardon. If there be any thing in this country I may please you in be pleased to command; it will be my ambition to serve you, nor shall I scruple to ride two or three hundred miles to satisfy any query you shall propound. If you honour me with your commands, you may direct your letter to Mr. *John Clayton*, parson of *James-City, Virginia*.

Your humble servant, and, though unknown, your friend,

John Clayton

[5] Essential oil?

[6] Crackling.

[7] Probably *Lytta vesicatoria*, a bright-green beetle of southern Europe. Dried and powdered, they were, and still are, used to raise blisters and are often called "blister beetles."

[8] This seems to have been the beginning of Clayton's friendship with Boyle. The interpretation which he sought has occupied a number of twentieth-century scientists.

[Enclosure[9]]

Maryland, Anno 1683

There happened about the month of November to one Madam Susanna Sewall, wife to Major Nic. Sewall,[10] of the Province abovesaid, a strange flashing of sparks (seemed to be of fire) in all the wearing apparel she put on, and so continued till Candlemas. And in the Company of several, Viz: Captain Edward Poulson, Captain John Harris,[11] Mr. Edward Braines,[12] the said Susanna did send several of her wearing

[9] This enclosure was in a letter from the Reverend Henry Miles, D.D. and F.R.S., to the president of the Royal Society, "containing observations of luminary emanations from human bodies and from brutes, with some remarks on electricity." It is here reprinted from *Phil. Trans.*, XLIII (1744–45), 441, where the following note by Dr. Miles appears:

"In the late edition of the works of the honorable Mr. Boyle, Vol. V., p. 646, is a letter from Mr. Clayton, dated June 23, 1684, at James City, in Virginia, in which he gives Mr. Boyle an account of a strange accident (as he calls it), and adds that he had inclosed the very paper Col. Digges gave him of it, under his own hand and name to attest the truth, and that the same was also asserted to him by Madame Digges, his Lady sister to the wife of Major Sewall, and daughter of the Lord Baltimore, to whom this accident happened. This paper very unhappily came not to hand till after Mr. Boyle's works were printed, and therefore could not be inserted with Mr. Clayton's letter. But having since met it, I present the following exact copy of it to you, and if you judge fit, by your hands to the Royal Society."

It has also been printed in the *William and Mary Quarterly*, ser. 1, IV (1896), 23, under the title of "Experience of Mrs. Elizabeth Diggs."

[10] Nicholas Sewall was a member of the Maryland Council. During Lord Baltimore's absence in England in 1689, the unpopularity of the acting governor, William Joseph, and a suspicion that the Roman Catholics were forming Indian alliances led to the "Protestant Rebellion." Digges surrendered and Sewall was forced to flee to Virginia.

[11] There was a John Harris who was granted 50 acres by Governor Leonard Calvert, father of the first Lord Baltimore. Harris had a son named John, but little is known of either (Forman, *Jamestown*, p. 302). Poulson remains unidentified.

[12] Possibly the man to whom William Byrd referred in the following passages, in his letters of March 31 and 29, 1685: "My Coz [Thomas] Grendon . . . dyed ye 10 of dr last at Sea & the Old Woman (not indureing to lye alone) Marryed abt ye latter end of Jan'ry to one Mr Edwd Brain a

apparel, and when they were shaken, it would fly out in sparks, and make a noise, much like unto bay leaves when flung into the fire, and one spark lit on Major Sewall's thumb nail, and there continued at least a minute before it went out, without any heat, all which happened in the company of Wm. Digges.

My Lady Baltimore, her Mother-in-law, for some time before the death of her son Caecelius Calvert, had the like happened to her, which has made Madam Sewall much troubled at what has happened to her. They carried Mrs. Susanna Sewall one day to put on her sister Digges' Petticoat, which they had tried beforehand and would not sparkle, but at night when Madam Sewall put it off, it would sparkle as the rest of her own garments did.

Stranger here." "Mr. Brain (who hath marry'd Mrs Grendon) pretends great matters though I cannot conceive wt incouragement they have found this year, comeing into the Country in Sept wth 30 Servants & 1000 or 1200£ of Goods, & could not (notwithstanding they tooke 100 Hds fraight) dispatch a Small ship of abt 350 or 360 Hds" (W. G. Stanard, "Letters of William Byrd, First," *Va. Mag. Hist. Biog.*, XXIV [1916], 236, 351).

III

"HINTS TO YOUR MORE PREGNANT REFLEXIONS"

Letter to Mr. Boyle, 1687[1]

Honour'd Sir

There is so mch tediousnesse, & trouble, in frequent removes, that I not only hope your pardon for so long demurage; But am confident you would rather pity me did you know the confusion I am involved in. The first hours I could call my own, are employed in observance of your commands, & they are happy interludes are diverted wth such desired such pleasing reflexions, not that I presume anything of my own thoughts are so takeing, but in serveing & obeying the commands of the honble Squire Boyle I receive so mch satisfaction. And tis therefore I the rather submit to your injunctions in obedience, more than out of fondnesse, as if anything that I can add should conduce to your noble performances. But not to trouble you wth a Tedious Apologie, but herein as well as in my Subsequent Notes, to be short, that wt may signify little may not give you mch trouble. If they suggest hints to your more pregnant reflexions, & evince that I'me yours to my utmost endeavour, I'me most happy in my wishes.

I shall not comment on evry note out of fondnesse to say

---

[1] Taken from the manuscript in the Archives of the Royal Society of London, Boyle Letters VI, item 62. Dr. R. E. W. Maddison, of Heston, Middlesex (who is presently editing the Boyle papers), very kindly brought this portion of a letter to our attention. As Clayton became rector of Crofton on July 2, 1687, this letter must have been written shortly thereafter.

somthing, but only on Such as particular experimts have suggested somthing new, wherefore I begin wth the third Quaere or Article:[2]

Quaere 3d. Whether Air be ingenerable, or incorruptible,[3] & whether it be producible by Art, or only extricable out of other bodys?

Sir Thomas Proby[4] a Gentleman of mch Study, & of a good genius, haveing heard of the New Digester wch I contrived,[5] had a desire to see it & some experimts made therein. I had a small one wch I designd only for an inward Cilinder; this I could easily put in my pocket wherefore goeing to pay him a visit at his house at Elton in Huntingdon Shire, I tooke it along wth me, & haveing softend a bone therein in a very short space, where at he mch admired, he was desirous to trie the shortest time it was possible to soften a bone in. I told him I thought I could soften the marrowbone of an Oxe in a very few minutes, but that that vessel was very weake, & I feard would not endure the pressure of so violent a heat. Yet he seemeing desirous to have the experimt tried I said I was ready to venture my vessel. Then haveing fixd all things right & included about a pint of water, & I believe about ℥ [two ounces] of a marrow bone. We put the vessel horizontally twixt the bars of the Iron grate into the fire about halfe way, & observd a minute watch, in 3 minutes time I found it raisd to a violent heat, whereupon I had a mind to have taken it forth of the fire, least that it should burst, telling Sir Thomas of the danger that

[2] Boyle seems to have given Clayton at least twenty-two questions on which he desired the latter's opinion.

[3] Shaw quotes Boyle as saying, "Many naturalists esteem the air to be ingenerable, and incorruptible, and plausible reasons may be drawn to countenance this opinion" (Shaw, *Boyle,* II, 429).

[4] See p. xxxv.

[5] Based on the Digester invented by Dr. Denis Papin. See pp. xxi–xxii.

I aprehended. For once the Screws of a Digester made after Mr. Papines Method giveing way, the head flew one way, the Screws & Irons another, & wth such violence, that fortunately there was no one in the Roome, otherwise it might have done mch hurt, the head hitt against a brick Stone, & cut a piece cleaverly out. Wch was one reason, & motive, to my contriveing of a digester this way, that the Scrues cannot possibly start, but the vessel would sooner break in any other part. But in this <I added> I thought the bottom would first burst, it being only Sauderd in, Scarse had I done speaking, & Sir Thomas thereupon removed his chair to avoid danger, but seeing the heat become more rageing I stepd to the Side table for the Iron wherewth I managed the digester, therewth to have taken it out of the fire. Wn on a Sudain it burst as if a musket had shot off, a maid that was gone a milking heard it at a considerable distance, the Servants said it shook the very house, as I had foretold the bottom of the vessel that was in the fire burst, the blast of the expanded water blowd all the coals out of the range all over the Roome, for the fire range was made just like an Oven, so that circulateing therein it brought forth all the Coales at the mouth thereof. All the vessel together flew in a direct line cross the Roome, & hitting the leafe of a table that was of an inch oake plank, broake it all in pieces, & rebounded halfe way of the Roome back again. Some of the Ashes as I suppose hit Sir Thomas' his knee, & made it swell immediately very mch, but by an immediat application it was reduced again very shortly, so that God be praisd there was no great harme. When it burst it came in my mind, in the first place to looke whether I could discerne any symptoms of the water, but could not find one drop of water, tho the vessel as I said contain a pint. I now leave it, Sir, to your consideration, whether it was the Elastick force of the Air extricated out of water, & dilated, that burst the vessel, or joyntly therewth the air generated from the water. I can hardly imagine how otherways a pint of water should in a moment passe away in vapour, this I think mch more considerable than the wind of an Eolipipe.[6] Since that seemes more a successive evapourateing of water, this is all at once in a moment, like the fireing off of Gunpouder, & wt conduces mch more to this sentiment, that air may be generated from water, or at least has in it an Elasticity, is the mch stronger Elastick force of air, & water joyntly included in a vessel, than wn air alone is inclosed therein, for the proof whereof I took two ʒvi [six-ounce] viols into the one I put about ʒv [five ounces] of water, or better, & so corckd it as well as possibly I could. The other I corckd in like maner wthout puting anything into it. I inclosed them both in the New Digester 4 fifths being fild wth water, when the heat was raised to about 5 seconds,[7] I heard a considerable explotion & a jingling of the glasse wthin the vessel, & shortly after another explotion, not so loud as the former, I concluded that both the glasses were broake, however I let the Digester coole leasurely & the next day opend it. Both the Corcks were swiming on the top of the water   That viol that I had not put any water into was burst, the other was whole: At first indeed I concluded that the pressure or dilata-

---

[6] The aeolipile, or aeolipyle, a pneumatic instrument, or toy, operated by the action of steam generated in a vessel closed except for a small opening or openings. It has taken many forms. This may be a reference to an experiment of Boyle's. Shaw quotes Boyle as follows: "But, to try whether water could be turn'd into air, we fill'd an aeolipile therewith; and placing it upon kindled coals . . ." (*Boyle*, II, 430).

[7] He surely means a longer time than this would suggest. He had his own "way of estimating the Degrees of Heat by Letting fall a drop of water from the same hight as it soaks from a wett Brown paper," according to the secretary of the Royal Society, who recorded his demonstration of the Digester on February 8, 1687/8 (Journal Book, VII [1686–90], 85–86, Archives of the Royal Society of London).

tion of the air in the empty viol, being stronger than the ambient[8] pressure, forced forth the Corck, whereupon the water rushing in knockd the weake viol in pieces & therefore this explotion was before the other, & made the louder explotion. But that the other being mostly filld wth water, tho the air forced forth the Corcke the bottle was thereby preservd. but I have had reason since to change my opinion. For haveing had very strong viols made on purpose, to make some peculiar experiments wth, A viol filld about a quarter full, corckd very well, & set in a Square Iron frame, wth a scrue to scrue down, & keep the corck for flying forth, I put it into the Digester, wch being heated to a due height. When I opend it, I found the Corck forced into the bottle, tho the Corck was so very large, that it amused many to conceive how it was possible so large a Corck should be forced into that bottle. This Experimt manifestly showed to me, that the pressure in the Digester wherein was proportionatly more water, & less air, to be stronger than the pressure wthin the viol wherein was proportionatly mch more air, & then I conceived thus of the 2 former viols. That the Air in the viol wherein was no water included, makeing not a proportionate pressure, to the ambient pressure in the Digester, wherein was a considerable quantity of water, the Corck was forced inward, wth such violence, that together wth the water it dashd the viol in pieces, & so the corck swam on the top of the water. But that in the other viol, wherein there was 5 Sixths of water, the inward pressure in the viol was greater than the ambient pressure in the Digester, the water being proportionatly more whereby the Corck was forced outward. But you, Great Sir, may perhaps find some better Solution. Yet if these Reasonings move you not to think that Air may be generated from

---

[8] Surrounding or encompassing.

water, I doubt not but I shall show it may be generated from
other Substances. Haveing then seen a Ditch wthin 2 miles of
Wigan in Lancashire,[9] wherein the water would seemingly
burn like brandy, so fierce, that several Strangers have boild
eggs over it, & as the people asserted that about 30 years since it
would have boild a piece of biefe, but that it was mch abated of
its violence, & that whereas mch rain formerly made it burn
mch fiercer, now after rain it would scarse burn at all. After a
long continued Seison of rain I calld to see the experimt &
found tho a lighted paper were waved all over the ditch, it
would not burn. I made the man to dam the Ditch, & fling out
the water, to trie whether any Steame that arose from the ditch
would then burn, but neither would yet anything catch fire. I
pursued still the experimt, & made him digg deeper & within
halfe a yard we found a shelly coale, the Candle being then put
down into the hole, the Air catchd fire, & continued burning,
there had formerly been Coalepitts in the same Close of
ground. Afterward I got some Coale from a pit very neare
thereunto, & destild in a Retort in an open fire. At first there
came over only Flegme, afterward a black oyle wth the
flegme,[10] & then likewise a Spt [spirit] arose wch I could no
ways condense,[11] but it forced my lute,[12] or broake my glasses,
then takeing a tubulated receiver, to the pipe I fixd a bladder
squeezed, & void of air, the oyle & flegme descended into the
receiver, the Spirit ascended, & blew up the blader therewth, I
fild many bladers, & might have fild an inconceivable number
more, for the Spt continued to rise Several hours, & fild the
bladers almost as fast as a man could have blown them, & yet
the quantity of coales were inconsiderable, I put a candle to
the pipe of the Receiver whilst the Spt arose, & it catchd flame,

[9] See pp. xxiii–xxiv.   [10] Coal tar.   [11] Coal gas.
[12] A substance, especially of clay, for sealing joints to make them impervious
to gas or liquids.

& continued burning at the end of the pipe, tho you could not discern what fed the flame, I blowd it out, & light it again several times, wch was very diverting, I kept of this Spt in bladers a considerable time, & endeavourd several ways to condense it, but in vain. And when I had a mind to divert Strangers or friends, takeing one of those blown bladders, & wth a pin pricking a hole or two, & compressing gently the bladder & so once lighting the Spt, it would flame as long as any Spt came forth, wch was surpriseing, & the more so cause no one could discerne any difference but as if they had been only blown wth common air. But then I found that this Spt must be kept in good thick bladers, as in those of an Oxe, or the like for if I filld Calfes bladers, it would loose its inflamability in 24 hours, tho the blader became not relaxe at all.[13] So that I concluded the inflamability proceeded but from the Subtiler parts of the oyle, that the Airy Spt had carryd along wth it, & that the Oyle of coales has strange subtile parts, is manifest hence, as well as from other proofes, that an earthern Bottle, tho very well glazed, will not keep it but it would grow thick & peirce the bottle. The Spt it selfe would answer all the trials of aire, that I could make but I refer it further to your consideration.

Quaere 17 of the heat & coldnesse of the air, as to its Regions & as to its Climes. The various alterations, & extent of the midle Region, I think depends not all together on heat, & Cold, since tis evidently mch lower in warm, & moist, than in cold sharp weather, wch is mch more notoriously remarkable in Virginia, than in England, for there a South East Wind, wch is very warm, covers the surface of the earth wth Clouds, & vailes it wth a thick fogg. But a Norwest even when it brings rain,

[13] Diffusion of the coal gas and gases of the atmosphere through the thinner bladders kept them inflated, but diluted their contents.

makes an elevated skie, & therefore those showers are more violent, & I believe very considerable remarkes might be made there wth the Barometer & Thermometer observeing as well the difference of the winds, as well as that of the wether, in the rise & fall of the Glasses, the oportunity of wch remarks I lost, by my glasses being all cast away. And I think it a great mistake in many that have gone to define the height of the Second Region,[14] by a single observation that they have made when they have ascended some very lofty mountain, & have discernd themselves as they thought at that time above any cloud, not to insist on the unsatisfactory method of their observations, grant that it were true that at that time they had been above the 2d. Region, it follows not that the Second Region may not at at [*sic*] another time reach so high, even in that place, mch lesse that it may not reach as high in other climes, nay in the same Clime, for in Different Countrys of the same latitude the Elemt <as tis cald>is mch higher in one place than another, & mch more in different Climes. And tis as remarkable that in the various degrees of longitude tho of the same latitude they differ signaly as to heat & cold, & the degree of 40 or at least of 45 in America is as cold as that of 50 in Europ

Quaere 22   Of the Saltnesse of the air, espetialy the Ejurine,[15] & the nitrous?   I remember an experimt wch I once made, sufficently manifested unto me the nitre[16] of the Aire, of wch Experiment tho the particular account was lost wth my other papers & books by Sea, yet I retain so perfect a remembrance

---

[14] A division of the atmosphere according to height.

[15] Aegirine (?).

[16] The term "nitre" (niter) usually refers to potassium nitrate (saltpeter) or sodium nitrate (Chile saltpeter). The chemical composition of air (approximately 78 per cent nitrogen, 21 per cent oxygen, and 1 per cent carbon dioxide and other gases) was not yet understood.

thereof as not to mistake in any material point. I tooke then a
small yellow gally pot,[17] such as the Northern Apothecarys use,
& ground the top of it very smooth, & true, & adapted a Cover
of Irish or blew Slat, wch I had likewise ground wth mch care,
into this gally pot I put equall quantitys of Nitre & flowers of
Sulphur,[18] about a ʒi [dram] of each. I then fixd on the Cover,
puting the gally pot into a Square Iron frame, wth a scrue, & so
put it into a New Digester. But the height I raisd the heat to,
& how long I continued it I do not so punctualy remember.
But believe it was to three or four Seconds, when I opend it the
day following, I perceivd somthing had transpired twixt the
top of the gally pot, & the cover, the top edges of the gally pot,
where the glazeing was ground of, being discoloured, but so
that the Nitre & Sulphurs were very little sensibly diminishd
as to their weight, only they were melted into one lump, wch I
took out of the Gally pot, that it seemd very cleane. Haveing
then other avocations that suddainly cald me abroad, for 3 or 4
days, I set this pot upon a Shelfe in another roome, viz my
study, & at my return goeing to make other experiments wth
the said Pot, I found long hoary hairs very bright, & brittle, all
round the ground edges of the Pot, very specious to behold,
after I had admired them a while, I gatherd them, & tasted
them & found them to be pure nitre.[19] I set the pot upon the
shelfe again to prosecute this experimt further, & in 3 or 4 days
more, found them shot again a 3d [*sic*] time, I set it up again &
gatherd them a 3d time as large & specious as at the first, so that
I suppose it would have continued to have shot fresh nitre mch
longer, had not I had urgent use for the Pot to make other

[17] Sometimes spelled "gallipot."
[18] Purified sulphur obtained by subliming (condensing without liquefying)
sulphur.
[19] The exposed (ground) edges of the pot apparently underwent some
chemical reaction with the atmosphere, probably with oxygen rather than
with the nitrogen, which is very inert.

experimts in, but I had gatherd more Nitre than I put into the
pot at first, tho as I sd before, for wt I could perceive, I had
taken all or neare all the nitre, that I put in together wth the
Sulphur out of the pot in Lump, hence we may have some
conceptions of the nature of mineral earths, & how they grow
when once impregnated wth the seeds of a mineral.   But for
the present purpose it mch more manifestly proves the nitre of
the Aire, since this can be supposed to be gatherd, & shoot
from the Aire only.

Haveing thus performd my promise tho perhaps not answerd
your expectations, I must assume a confidence whereunto I'me
carryd by impetuous desires & tis to Challenge your promise
that you will honour me wth a line   pardon me Sir for I must
remind you of wt you was most obligeingly pleasd to offer, to
communicate some receits & secrets wch you said you would
not trust to the hazards of a letter but under a hidden Character the key of wch you sd you would send me in the first place.[20]
If Sir you may well deeme me worthy of so mighty a favour
assure your selfe they shall be kept secret as your commands.
From Huntingdon Shire I sent you a Draught of the Speakeing
trumpet[21] wch if you sent to his Majestie as you told me you
designed I should be glad to hear wt acceptance it found.   And
now Sir Ime about building a furnace to Draw some of that Spt
for you wch I told you of, forr before this I have had no
oportunity   all my Retorts being broake in Huntingdon Shire
by the Winds shakeing the house whilst I was at London.
During my stay in Huntingdon shire I had further proofe of its
virtues for haveing some left wch I thought too ill drawn to

[20] Boyle had been much disturbed by the stealing of his writings. See p.
xxxviii.

[21] Clayton referred to this "Speakeing trumpet" in the account of his voyage
to Virginia (p. 42) .

present you wth I did many cures wth it.   A young man that
had a lamenesse & a great Swelling in his knee wth violent
pains like that of a Sciatica pain   It had continued 12 years tho
he had had many able Phisitians that had in vain attempted a
cure, in a fortnights time I so reduced it that he could readily
walk 3 or four miles together & few could discern that he
halted   he could stand on that legg alone bearing his whole
body boldly thereon without pain   he used mch violent exercise afterwards wthout anything of a Relaps.   I have great
confidence I may therewth cure the gout from the several
effects I have seen wrought by it.   But Ime now in a Country
where I'me afraid I shall not have such oportunitys to improve
it, liveing Solitary in a little Hamlet, pleasd only wth the
recollection on those happy hours I enjoyd in your con-
versa[tion.]

IV

"THE ABORIGINES OF THE COUNTRY"

Letter to Dr. Nehemiah Grew[1]

A letter from the Revd Mr: John Clayton afterwards Dean of Kildare in Ireland to Dr. Grew, in answer to several Querys sent to him by that learned gentleman.   A. D 1687.

Communicated by the Right Revd Father in God Robt. Lord Bp of Corke to John Earl of Egmont F. R. S.[2]

I have observed many gross mistakes in peoples notions of Virginia, when descoursing of the natives, which have arisen, from the want of making a distinction in their Expressions, when they speak of the English or Whites born there & so called *Natives;* & the *Aborigines* of the Country.   Please therefore to take notice that when I speak of the natives in general that I mean only the Indians.

As therefore to your first Quaere.   Their *Wiochist,* that is, their Preist is generally their Physician & is a person of the greatest honour & esteem among them, next to the King, or to their great War-Captain.

2.   Nature is their great Apothecary, each Physician furnishing himself, according to his skill, with Herbs or the

[1] 1641–1712, noted plant anatomist and active fellow of the Royal Society.

[2] Taken from Bishop Clayton's copy of his father's manuscript, in Papers Relating to the Royal Society, B.M., Birch Collection 4437, f. 398. This version differs somewhat in spelling, punctuation, and a few phrases from the letter as published in *Phil. Trans.,* XLI (1739), 143–62 (see Plate I, facing p. 32) It also appeared in D. I. Bushnell, "Virginia from Early Records," *American Anthropologist,* IX (1907), 31–45.

leaves, fruit roots or barks of trees, of which he sometimes
makes use of the Juice & sometimes reduces them into Powder
or perhaps makes a decoction thereof.

3.   Though every one according to his skill is a sort of
Doctor <as many women are in England> yet their Preist is
peculiarly stiled their Physician, to be consulted upon greater
Emergencys. The rules of the descent hereof as to familys, I
do not know, for they are a sullen close people & will answer
very few questions.

4.   They reward their Physician with no certain fees, but
according as they bargain for Wampam peake³ skins or the
like; if it be to an Englishman they are sent for, they will agree
for a Match coat or a gallon or two of Rum or so forth
according to the nature of the cure. Sometimes the Preist will
sell his remedy, for some of them have told me that they have
bought the root which cures the bite of the Rattle Snake from
their *Wiochist.*

5.   Their King allows no sallary, that ever I heard of, but
every one that in any nature can serve his Prince, is ready to do
it, & to do it gratis.

6.   They have no consultations, their practice being merely
Empirical. They know little of the nature or reason of
things. Ask them any question about the operation of a remedy, & if in good humour, perhaps they will reply, *it cures;*
otherwise they will shrugg their shoulders, & you may ask 40
questions & not know whether they understood the thing, or
what it is that you say to them.

7.   They pay a certain deference of honour to their Preist
or Wiochist, whose person they hold sacred. But laws they have
none <as far as I could ever learn> that binds them thereto;
in general the will of their Prince stands for reason & Law.

8.   The means whereby they convey their art to Posterity, I

³ Wampum.

take to be this. They lodge in their Wiochisan houses, i. e. their temples, certain kinds of reliques, such as men's skulls some certain grains or pulse,[4] & several herbs which are dedicated to their Gods. Viz the skulls in memory of their fights & Conquests. The pulse by way of thank-offering for their provisions, & the Herbs upon the same account for some special cure performed thereby. For when any one is cured by any herb he brings part thereof & offers it to his God, whereby the remembrance of this herb & its virtue is not only preserved: But the Preist also becomes best instructed thereby & knowing in the art of medicine.[5] For otherwise they are mighty reserved of their knowledge even among themselves. Whether the Preist takes certain persons to instruct or teaches only his own children I know not. Often when they are abroad hunting in the woods & fall sick or come by any hurt, they then are forced to make use of any herbs which are nearest at hand, which they are not timorous in venturing upon though they know not the virtue or quality thereof, & thus by making many trials & experiments, they find out the Virtues of Herbs & by using simple remedys, they certainly know what it is that effects the cure.

9.   They are generally most famed for curing of wounds. They have indeed various very good wound-herbs, as an Herb commonly called *Indian-weed,* which perhaps may be referred to the *Valerians,* & be said to be *Platani foliis.*[6] They use also the *Gnafolium Americanum*[7] commonly called the *white*

---

[4] Seeds of beans, peas, and other legumes.

[5] This was not unlike the maintenance of herbaria of drug plants by Europeans.

[6] An unidentified member of the Valerianaceae, with leaves like those of the plane tree (similar to our sycamore).

[7] Possibly *Gnaphalium obtusifolium* L., rabbit tobacco, sweet everlasting, which is used today for treatment of pulmonary and intestinal catarrh, diarrhea, and bruises.

Plaintain. As to our Plantain[8] or the Heptapleuron they call
it the *Englishman's foot,* & have a tradition that it will only
grow where they have troden, & was never known before the
English came into this Country. The most famous old Physician among the *Apomatick Indians,* as I was informed by a
person of a very good understanding, used mostly an Herb
which he showed me, whose leaf is much like *self-heal*[9] in
Winter. I observed it was red underneath & would at length
appear tinged on the upper side also, it makes a good salve only
it fills a wound too fast with flesh. I took a draught of this
herb along with some others which I have left in the North of
England. The greatest success they have is curing wound and
sores, I apprehend mostly to proceed from their manner of
dressing them: For they first cleanse them by sucking, which
though a very nasty, is no doubt the most effectual & best way
imaginable; then they take the biting Persicary[10] & chaw it in
their mouths, & thence squirt the Juice thereof into the
wound, which they will do as if it were out of a syringe. Then
they apply their salve-herbs, either bruised or beaten into a
salve with grease, binding it on with bark & silk grass. Coll
Spencer[11] the present Secretary of State of Virginia told me of a
very strange & extraordinary cure performed by an Indian, on
one of his Negros. The Negro was a very good servant,
wherefore his master had valued him much, but by degrees he
grew dim-sighted, & was troubled with terrible pains in his
eyes, so that with one he could see but a little & none at all with
the other, and as the pain encreased the Coll was greatly
apprehensive least his Negro would be quite blind. Several

[8] *Plantago major* L., common plantain or white man's foot, introduced into
the United States from Europe.

[9] *Prunella vulgaris* L.   [10] *Persicaria* L., smartweed.

[11] Nicholas Spencer, relative of Lord Culpeper, who appointed him acting
governor.

Surgeons were sent for who had tried to cure him, but in vain.
When an Indian coming to the house, said he could cure him,
they told Mr Secretary thereof, who sent for the Indian &
agreed with him for 2 quarts of Rum. The Indian told him
that he could save the one eye, but that the Negro would be
blind in the other. The next morning the Indian went a
hunting into the woods for his herbs, & returned with them
about noon, which he bruised, putting thereto a little water; &
having pressed forth some of the Juice, he dropped some
thereof into the eye which he said would be blind, & laid the
herbs thereon, which he would have bound fast with bark, but
the Coll called for some linnen rags & had it bound up
therewith. He then intimated to the Coll that shortly after
the sun sett the Negro would be mad, if his medicine took
effect, but would come to himself again before morning.
Therefore strict orders were given that he should be well
attended, & that nothing should be alter'd lett what would
happen. All things therefore being accordingly done as the
Indian had directed, every thing proceeded likewise as the
Indian had foretold. Then about eleven o'clock the next day,
the binding being removed & the herbs taken off from the eye,
the Indian bid the Negro hold down his head, which when he
had done out drops the Christaline & aequaeous humours.[12]
The Indian afterwards bound it up again, & by degrees the
Negro was freed from his pain, & had perfect sight with the
other eye. What the Herbs were the Coll could never learn
from him, though he proffered him whatever he would de-
mand.

10.   The distempers among the English-Natives <for I
cannot give to[o] particular an account of the distempers
most predominant among the Indians> are *scorbutical-*

---

[12] "Christaline" refers to the crystalline lens; the aquaeous humours are
fluids in the cavity between the lens and the cornea.

Dropsys, Chachexies, Lethargys, Seasonings,[13] which are an intermiting feaver, or rather a continued feaver with quotidian paroxisms. These are now rarely sharp, but show themselves in a lingering sickness. The *griping of the guts* mostly dry & when tormina ventris[14] cease, they generally shoot into the limbs, & fix there, in a terrible sort of gout, taking away the use of the limbs. Thus they will pine away to skin & bone so that their joynts will seem dislocated, & their hands utterly crippled. Sore throats which the last year were very frequent, & seemed infectious, running generally through whole familys, & unless early prevented became a cancerous humour, & had effects like the French Pox.[15] Likewise *Pains in the Limbs,* which I apprehend to have proceeded partly from the same humour floating up and down the body, these pains are very exquisite, mostly nocturnal, for while they walk if they have the use of their limbs, they feel the least pain. The oyl of a fish called a *Drum*[16] was found very effectual to cure these pains, & restore the limbs. I was eye witness when a very worthy gentlewoman who had lost the use of her limbs was entirely recovered by the use of this medicine. For her feet being anointed with this oyl the pains flew into her head, her head thereupon being anointed the pain descended again, then anointing both head and feet she was recovered. There are 3 sorts of oyls in that Country, whose Virtues if fully proved might not perhaps be found despicable; The oyle of *Drums,* the oyle of Rattlesnake, & the oyl of *Turky Bustards.* The oyl of *Sassafras leaves* may be deservedly considered too, for they

[13] Scorbutical dropsy, a scurvy type of dropsy; cachexies, general ill health; lethargies, lassitude from physical or mental disability.

[14] Lead colic, see p. 4, n. 3.

[15] Scarlet fever or diphtheria? French pox was syphilis.

[16] There are a number of fish which are commonly called "drum" or "drum-fish" because of the drumming noises they make. Common on the Atlantic coast are *Pogonias cromis* and *Sciaenops ocellata.*

will almost entirely dissolve into an oyle.[17]   But to return there is another sort of distemper which I judge to be the *Lepra Grecorum*,[18] and it may perhaps be no bad conjecture that this chiefly proceeds from their feeding so much as they do, on a delicate caseious[19] sort of Pork.   Among the Indians they have a distemper which they call the *Yaws*,[20] which is nearly related to the *french Pox;* which they are said to cure with an herb that Fluxes them, but this I have only by hear-say.

11.   The Indians mind neither the pulse nor Urine only judge by the common most remarkable symptoms, & some pretend to form a judgement from the Countenance, & are fond of being thought Physiognomists.

12.   I never could find that they practised the *letting of blood*. They purge much with several sorts of roots of their own country growth & vomit frequently with various herbs. They Sweat boldly and excessively, & after a very strange manner: For they have their sweating stones always upon the bank of some River, whence they rush forth in the height of their sweat, & run into the River, where they wash & bath themselves very plentifully.[21] They use no *blistering plasters,* but are exquisite at Cupping;[22] as the East Indans use Moxa, so these burn with Punk, which is the inward part of the excrescence, or exuberance of an Oak.[23] When they design to give a

[17] Sassafras oil is today used as an antiseptic in sprays, a stimulant, a diaphoretic, and an ant repellent. Blanton has stated that it was extremely popular as a stimulant and as an astringent in the seventeenth century (*Medicine in Virginia*, p. 109).

[18] A class of scaly skin affections, mostly psoriasis.

[19] Caseous, meaning cheesy.

[20] Frambesia, a contagious skin disease resembling syphilis, still known as "yaws."

[21] Their sweat lodges must have resembled the Finnish sauna.

[22] Drawing blood to the surface by forming a partial vacuum over a spot.

[23] Leaves of *Artemisia moxa* were formed into a mat and burned on the skin as a cautery. "Punk" can refer to decayed wood or to some fungi, used as tinder.

Purge, they make use of the following herbs. *Poake-root* i:e: *Solanum Baciferum,* a strong purge, & by most deemed poison.[24] The roots of *Tythemel*[25] of which I have observed two sorts. The one *flore minimo herbacio,* the other *flore albo,* the flower of this last is small but large in comparison with the other: they are *repentes,*[26] & grow in old manured grounds. They chiefly make use of the latter of these, & it is a most excellent purge, though it sometimes Vomits; It is a quick but moderate worker enough, & has this peculiarity, that it opens the body in the *Gripes,* when other much violenter purgatives will not move it. There is another herb which they call the *Indian purge,*[27] this plant has several woody stalks, growing near 3 feet tall, & as I remember *perfoliat,* it bears yellow berrys, round about the joynts, they only make use of the Root of this plant. They use also the *small flower de Lice,* whose virtues I believe are not yet half known, for it has some extraordinary qualitys; It does not grow above an hand high, flowers in March & is very fragrant.[28] They use also some sort of *Apocinums,*[29] particularly that which I think Gerard calls *Vincetoxicum Americanum,* for there are several sorts of Apocinums', I think thirteen or fourteen, but they are not all purgative. For having got some of the root from an Indian which he assured me was the *Rattlesnake root,* I thought the root of an *Apocinum* <which may well be distinguished by

[24] Probably *Phytolacca americana* L., whose roots are now used as an emetic and in the treatment of rheumatism. It is commonly known as "pokeroot" or "American nightshade."

[25] Probably *Euphorbia ipecacuanhae* L. (*Tithymalopsis* Small), wild ipecac, or related species having emetic properties.

[26] Trailing or creeping.

[27] Species of *Gillenia* are now commonly called "Indian physic," but they do not fit Clayton's description very well.

[28] Fleur-de-lis, *Iris verna* L.

[29] Apocynaceae or dogbane family, possibly *Apocynum cannabinum* L. (dogbane or Indian hemp), valued as a heart stimulant and diuretic. John Gerard (1545–c.1611) was a well-known herbalist.

that of Rosae Marie folis> was very like it, both in shape &
taste, considering the one dried & the other fresh. Wherefore I
gott some quantity thereof, & carrying it in my pocket, I ven-
tured to eat thereof little by little, till I believe I have taken a
dram at a time, to observe if it had any peculiar operation on
the body, but could never find that it had.

They have likewise several sorts of herbs wherewith they
vomit, one of which is a little sort of Squills.[30] They likewise
take the leaves of a certain curious odoriferous shrub, that
grows in the swamps, which I take to be the *lesser sassafras*,[31]
they bruise them in water, & then express the juice, which they
drink warm. The Indian interpreter who taught me this,
prized it much as excellent Physick, & said they found it a very
sovereign remedy. It is as odoriferous as any shrub I ever
smelt at in my life, whoever has once taken notice of the smell
cannot forget it, or be deceived therein afterwards, having
something peculiar in it. The name which the Indian gave
me hereof was *Wisechis,* which since I understand is the
general word for Physick.

13. The rest of the *materia medica* consists of herbs, of
which they have a great plenty, & seldom prescribe any thing
else. I have collected above 300 several sorts that were no
European plants, but I shall only mention those at present,
whose virtues I take to be most remarkable. And First the
Sassafras tree,[32] whose root is well enough known. It shoots
forth its blossoms in March which are yellow & grow in
little bunches like grape-flowers, & which when gathered
& picked from the husky bud, make a curious preserve.
Most Sassafras trees blossom, few bear berrys, but those

[30] *Camassia scilloides* (Raf.) Cory, from the East Indian word *camass.*
[31] Possibly *Lindera benzoin* (L.) Blume., spicebush, feverbush, or wild all-
spice, a genus closely related to *Sassafras.*
[32] *Sassafras albidum* (Nutt.) Nees. See note 17.

that do are generally very thick, they are shaped much like those of *Dulcamara*,[33] but are black of colour & very *aromatick*, I take them to have considerable virtues. The *Gum-tree* which I refer to the species of Plain-trees, & distinguish it by its figg like leaf, only more sharply dented. Its leaf smells much like a Lemon. Their practice is to beat the tree & then pill off the bark & so scrape the Gum, which has virtues like Terpentine or rather more astringent & drying. This they usually mix with their common Terpentine which is whiter & more butter-like than the Venice or Chios Terpentine.[34] Quaere whether better or No? The further method of preparing this medicine, as I am told is this. They expose it to the sun on paper, where at first it rather seems to melt, but it will afterwards grow hard, they then beat it to a powder & administer it. They use much the young budds of the *Populus sive Tulippa arbor*,[35] a vast large tree extraordinary specious, bearing flowers about April much like Tulips, its leaves are large, smooth & well shaped, which together with the flowers, render the tree exceedingly beautiful to behold. It bears its seed coniferous, & is an excellent opener of Obstructions. The *Sorrell tree*[36] bears a leaf something like a Laurel, in taste much resembling *Lujula*.[37] They use it in feavers, & as I am informed, with good success. This tree grows plentifully on the South side of James river in Virginia. I cannot say I ever found it to the Northward. The *Swamp-*

[33] *Solanum dulcamara* L., bittersweet or nightshade.

[34] *Liquidambar styraciflua* L., sweet gum. It furnishes a balsam called "American storax," used as a stimulating expectorant and as a perfume for soaps, etc. Chios turpentine is made from the oleaginous resin of the terebinth, *Pistacia terebinthus*.

[35] *Liriodendron tulipifera* L., tulip poplar or tulip tree. It is actually a magnolia rather than a poplar.

[36] *Oxydendrum arboreum* (L.) DC., sourwood, having sour-tasting leaves and white flowers, but the leaves do not resemble laurel.

[37] Lujula was an old name for wood sorrel, *Oxalis*.

Plumb-tree[38] whose wood they calcine, & make into charcoal, which they beat to a powder, then mix it with grease, & make an oyntment thereof, with which they anoint the body, & foment it very much, whereby they cure the *Dropsy*. For it opens the pores, to that degree, that the water runs down their leggs. Among their herbs I have had 40 several sorts or near that number showed me as great secrets, for the *Rattle-snake root*, or that kind of *Snakeroot* which is good for curing the bite of the *rattlesnake*. But I have no reason to believe that any of them are able to effect the cure. One gentleman showed me a certain root which was a *Smilax*,[39] and assured me that that was certainly the *Rattle snake root*. And afterwards when I showed Mr Secretary Spencer the same root he said that certain Indians had given him of the same root for the Rattle-snake root & that he had some quantity to send for England, but this root is by no means the same with that which I have mentioned before in answer to Quaere 12, which I said was like the root of an Apocinum, which I myself obtained from an Indian, who seemed to prize it highly, having sowed it care-fully up in leather, on the inside of his belt. Others have showed me *Chrysanthemum ferulaceis foliis* for it. Others *Chrysanthemum tragophei foliis*.[40] Again general report goes in favour of the Asarum Syclaminis foliis,[41] which many there-fore particularly call *Rattlesnake root*. There are strange stories told in favour of an herb called *Ditany*, which however is not of the Ditany kind, but is only a Mountain Calaminth.

[38] This may have been any one of several species of *Prunus*.

[39] Linnaeus gave the name to the greenbrier or catbrier, but the false Solomon's-seal, *Smilacina* was once called "*Smilax*." Some South and Central American *Smilax* species are our source of sarsaparilla and also are used in the treatment of rheumatism, syphilis, and psoriasis.

[40] Clayton emphasizes the confusion which can result from the common names for plants or animals.

[41] *Asarum*, wild ginger, or heartleaf, some species of which have leaves very like those of *Cyclamen*.

This they say will not only cure the bite of a Rattle-snake but that the smell thereof will kill the snake.[42]   But however though I have some reason to believe that this herb will not cure the bite, nor that the smell thereof will kill the snake. <For Coll Spencer, a Gentleman of erudition had an opportunity of making an experiment thereof upon a Dog which was bitten by a Rattlesnake to whom he gave plentifully of the juice of this Dittany as they called it, but the dog died never the less a day or two after and Mr Wormley,[43] one of the Council of State in Virginia, told me that being in company with another gentleman he had an opportunity of making the following experiment, For seeing a rattle-snake in her coil they went and got a bunch of this Dittany & tied it to a pole, then putting the Dittany that was thereon to the nose of the snake, it seemed to offend her, whereupon she turned away her head, which they still followed with the Dittany, then the snake fled, & they still pursuing her, she at last stretched her self out at length & lay seemingly dead; then they laid their Dittany upon her head & went into a neighboring house to refresh themselves, for they were tired with skipping about after the snake; when they had staid near half an hour, they returned to see their supposed dead snake, but behold that the snake was fled. So that they then judged that the snake had only stretched herself out, because she had been tired with their pursuit.   I

[42] *Cunila origanoides* (L.) Britt. is known as common dittany, but Clayton probably referred to *Hedeoma pulegiodes* (L.) Pers., pennyroyal. In 1665 Captain Silas Taylor gave a talk on the power of "Wild Penny-royal" or "Dittany of Virginia," which was used in 1657 to kill a snake ("Of a Way of Killing Rattle-Snakes," *Phil. Trans., I* [1665], 43).   Thomas Glover described it as 12–18 inches high, with leaves the width of a groat and shaped like a heart and branches opposite each other.   He said it smelt like hot pepper, was a good vermifuge, and excellent in producing sweating (*Phil. Trans.,* XI [1676], 623–36).

[43] Ralph Wormeley (1650–1701), president of the Council, in whose home, Rosegill, Governor Effingham stayed.

I. *A Letter from the Rev^d Mr.* John Clayton, *(afterwards Dean of* Kildare *in* Ireland*) to Dr.* Grew, *in Anfwer to feveral Queries relating to* Virginia, *fent to him by that learned Gentleman, A.* D. 1687. * *communicated by the Right Reverend Father in God* Robert *Lord Bifhop of* Corke, *to* John *Earl of* Egmont, F. R. S.

I Have obferved many grofs Miftakes in Peoples Notions of *Virginia*, when difcourfing of the Natives, which have rifen from the want of making a Diftinction in their Expreflions, when they fpeak of the *Englifh* or *Whites*, born there, and fo called *Natives*; and the *Aborigines* of the Country. Pleafe therefore to take Notice, that when I fpeak of the Natives in general, I mean only the *Indians*.

As therefore to your firft Query : Their *Wiochift*, that is, their Prieft, is generally their Phyfician ; and is a Perfon of the greateft Honour and Efteem among them, next to the King, or to their great War-Captain.

2. Nature is their great Apothecary, each Phyfician furnifhing himfelf, according to his Skill, with Herbs, or the Leaves, Fruit, Roots, or Barks of Trees ; of which he fometimes makes ufe of the Juice, and fometimes reduces them into Powder, or perhaps makes a Decoction thereof.

3. Though every one, according to his Skill, is a fort of Doctor, (as many Women are in *England*

---

* This may ferve as a Sequel to the Accounts of *Virginia* formerly given by Mr. *Clayton*. See thefe *Tranfactions*, N° 201. 205, 206. 210.

T

yet

Plate I. Clayton's letter (1687) to Nehemiah Grew as it appeared in *Philosophical Transactions*, XLI (1739), 143–62. [See p. 21.]

Plate II. Last page of Clayton's letter of August 17, 1688, to the Royal Society. [See p. 90.] (Archives of the Society)

look upon it probable therefore that some accident of the like
kind may have first given origin to this story, the person who
had tired the snake not having regularly waited for the Event,
but perhaps to secure the Contest may have given the snake a
stroke with a switch upon the back, which would have killed
the snake without the Dittany.> But yet never the less this
plant is of more than ordinary virtue & might not unprofitably
be used by our Physicians, it may be referred to the Class of the
Calamintha montana Pulegii odore which has been transferred from thence into England, & I think is now pretty
common, but is better & more sudorifick.

I will now mention to you an herb though unknown, yet
worthy to be fetched from Virginia yielded the Country nothing else, it is the herb called there *Angelica*,[44] but which I take
to be *Libanotis vera latifolia Dodones*. It grows generally on a
rich sandy ground, on a declining brow, that faces the rising
sun, the root shoots deep into the earth, sometimes near 3 feet,
very tender & easily broken, of a white or rather cream-like
colour, & being lactescent, yields a little milk thick & yellow as
cream, a very early plant, it seldom flowers or seeds under 5
years growth; for I have fully and distinctly observed that
number of years, in the several sorts of this plant, by the
growth of those not come to maturity to bear seed, and it is
observable that those which do not seed have rarely more than
one branch which divides when it spreads, & subdivides itself,
still into 3, the leaf is much like our wild Angelica only thinner
& more the colour of willow-green. Those that seed have a
fistelous stalk about the thickness of *Dill*,[45] a white umbellifer-
ous plant, the seeds are much like Angelica seed, but from the
fragrancy of the root & its being peculiarly bearded, I un-

[44] Possibly *Angelica atropurpurea* L. *Angelica venenosa* (Greenway)
Fern. is also found in eastern Virginia, but is considered to be very poisonous.
[45] *Anethum graveolens* L.

doubtedly stile it a *Libanotis*. It stops the Flux & cures it to a
wonder; again it often loosens & purges the bodys of those that
are bound, & have the gripes especially if it proceed from cold;
& prevents many unhappy distempers; I have reason to speak
well of it, for it is to it, under God, that I attribute the saving of
my own life. I have known it give 14 or 15 stools, whereas it
will not move a child in health. I take it to be the most
sovereign remedy the world ever knew in the griping of the
guts & admirable against Vapours,[46] it is suderifick[47] & very
aromatick, & will not be concealed for wherever it is mixed it
will leave the predominant scent. It is mostly called by those
who know it in Virginia, by the name of *Angelica*. But
showing a piece of the root to a great Woodsman to see
whether he knew it & could tell me where it grew. He seemed
surprised to see me have thereof, & told me that he kept an
Indian once for some weeks with him, because he was an
excellent woodsman, & going a hunting <i:e:> shooting they
came where some of this root grew; The Indian rejoicing
gathered some of it, but was very careful to cut off the top of
the root and replant it; He then asked him why he was so
carefull, whereunto the Indian replyed, It was a very choice
plant & very scarce for they sometimes travelled 100 or 200
miles without finding any of it. He then asked him what use it
was of, to which the Indian answered you shall see by and by.
After some time they spyed 4 Deer at a distance, then the
Indian contrary to his usual custom went to windward of
them, & sitting down upon an old trunk of a Tree, began to
rub the root betwixt his hands, at which the Deer toss up their
heads & snuffing with their noses they fed towards the place
where the Indian satt, till they came within easy shot of him,
whereupon he fired at them, & killed a large buck. The truth
of this story I no further assert than that I was told it by a

[46] Hypochondria or melancholy.   [47] Causing or inducing sweat.

person of seeming seriousness who had no inducement to tell a lie or impose upon me. But I have often taken notice that the Indians call it the *Hunting root,* which makes me more inclinable to give credence to this story. Another Gentleman a white native of that Country when I once pulled a piece of the root out of my pocket to bite thereof, for I frequently carry'd some of it about me, asked me if I loved fishing. I required wherefore he asked me that question? Because said he you have gotten some of the fishing root. The fishing root! replyed I. Pray why do you give it that name? Because said he when we were boys we used to get some of it to lay with our baits to invite the fish to bite. This I can say of my own knowledge that having one day got some quantity of the root, & likewise of the branches to distill the strong scent as I went home palpably putt me into a breaking sweat, in the night I was waked by a Rat which ran over my face, whereas I never at any other time had the like happen to me, but will not be positive to conclude that this root was the cause thereof, only the precedent relations made me reflect thereon. There is another root of the Species of Hyacinths, the leaves whereof are grass-like but smooth & stiff, of a willow-green colour, & spreads like a star upon the ground, from the middle shoots a tall long rush-like stem, without leaves, near two feet high on one side grow little white bell flowers one above another. The root is black outwardly, but brown within. It is bitter & I take it to have much the same virtues with *little Century.* Some call it *Ague-grass,* others *ague root,* others *Star grass.*[48] I have likewise been told by several of a root which the Indians cure bruises wonderfully with, but I apprehend it as the same root with which the Indian cured the Negro's Eye aforementioned: for it operates much after the same manner according to their relation, making the Patient mad for some hours, if they be

[48] *Aletris farinosa* L.

recoverable. It is not to be apply'd where the skin is broken, they use it thus. They chaw some of the root in their mouths, & then squirt it forth on the bruised part, fomenting it well with their hands, then they give a little to the person bruised to chaw, who must swallow the juice, but spit forth the root again, which they bind on the part agrieved. If the relations I have had of cures performed thereby, be absolutely true, the world has not yet discovered a more wonderfull remedy. I had it described to me by Coll Smith[49] of the Isle of Wight County, to be like *Langue de boeuf,*[50] with a yellow flower, & ruff hoary leaf, the root yellowish, & tasted something sweetish like Liquerish. There are several others, I might name, whose virtues are by no means despicable, such as the *Chrysanthemum Platani foliis* whose root is very usefull in *old pains,* the *Sciatica* & *Gout.* It is a large herb grows betwixt 5 & 6 feet tall. There are likewise many others which bear some analogy to the European plants, such as *Solomon's-Seal,*[51] *Wood-sage,*[52] much better I think than the English, which the Indians use much for Infusions, & which they take as we do diet-drink. *Little Century,*[53] red, white & yellow etc. However, I never could find above 12 or 14 plants which were natives of that country, that agreed perfectly with any of our European plants, but what had some notable differences, if they were not rather to be reckoned a distinct Genus.

13. [This number was used twice.]   There go traditions of their having an art to poison their darts, but I could never find

[49] Colonel Nicholas Smith.

[50] The name *Langue de boeuf* has been applied to a number of different plants including *Echium vulgare, Helminthia echioides,* and *Borago officinalis.* Clayton's description suggests one of the gromwells, possibly *Onosmodium virginianum* (L.) A. DC.

[51] Species of *Polygonatum* L. or *Smilacina* Desf.

[52] *Teucrium canadense* L.

[53] Not identified. Possibly *Centaurea,* which does have flowers of these colors.

any solid grounds for that report. I have observed that, in those Countrys upon an ill habit of body, the least scratch is dangerous, & that for all the care that can be taken to prevent it, it often turns into a very desperate ulcerous sore. Some herbs there are of an analagous nature with Hemlock,[54] whereof I think they know nothing further than that they are to avoid them. But any herbs wherewith they poison their darts I never could hear specify'd. And as persons engaged in long marches are liable to many accidents which may contribute to an ill state of health, when a slight wound in battle has then proved mortal this I apprehend to have been the Cause why the Physician has rather chosen to attribute the death of his patient to the poison of the dart, than the want of skill in himself.

14.   As to their morals they are simple & credulous, rather honest than otherwise, & unpracticed in the European art of lying & dissimulation; but as to the brutal passions they are sottish & sensual as the beast of the field.

15.   They are almost allways either eating or sleeping unless when they go a Hunting, at all hours of the night whenever they are awake they go to the *Hominy-pot,* that is, maze dressed in a manner like our pilled wheat,[55] or else a piece of Venison *barbecuted,* that is wrapped up in leaves & roasted in the Embers.

16.   They drink I think little besides *Succahannah* that is fair water, unless when they can gett spirits, such as Rum, from the English, which they will allways drink to excess if they can possibly get them, but do not much care for them unless they can have enough to make them drunk, & I have heard it said that they wonder much at the English for purchasing wine at

[54] *Conium maculatum* L., poison hemlock, a native of Europe but naturalized in North and South America.

[55] I.e., peeled or pared off or with the hull removed.

so dear a rate when Rum is much cheaper & will make them sooner drunk.

17.   They use tobacco much, which they smoak in short pipes, of their own making, having excellent clay, which I tried a little, before I came for England, making crucibles thereof which I could not discern were inferior to the German. They make also neat pots of the same clay which will endure the fire for any common uses.

18.   They have no *Opium* though in some old fields upon York River I found Poppys perhaps of no despicable virtue. I have been told that in feavers & when their sick cannot sleep they apply the flowers of *Strammonium*[56] to the Temples, which has an effect like *Laudanum*. I have had asserted by many that when the soldiers were sent over to quel the Insurrection of Bacon etc. They being at Jamestown several of them went to gather a sallet in the fields & lighting in great quantitys on an herb called *Jamestown-Weed*, they gathered it, & by eating thereof in plenty were rendered apish & foolish as if they had become drunk or were become Idiots. Dr Lee[57] likewise assured me that the same accident happened once in his own family, but that after a night or two's sleep they recovered

19.   Their *Sports* are dancing, their *Games* are playing with straws, which as I am not perfectly acquainted with I find it hard to describe, I can therefore only tell you how it appears to a looker-on. They take a certain number of straws, & spread them in their hands, holding them as if they were cards,

[56] *Datura stramonium* L., Jamestown weed or jimson weed. It is not clear that Clayton realized that *Stramonium* and Jamestown weed were the same plant. This is still widely used as a drug plant. The drug has properties similar to those of belladonna.

[57] Probably Dr. George Lee who "practised in Surry County from 1673 or earlier, until 1680, when he was granted a lease of two houses and fifty acres at Jamestown" (Blanton, *Medicine in Virginia*, p. 277).

then they close them, & spread them again & turn them very suddenly, & seem very dextrous thereat. Their Exercise is hunting that is, shooting with a gun, or with Bow & arrow wherein they excel. Their women work, plant the corn, & weave baskets or matts.

20.　　Several have been very old, I cannot say that herein there is any remarkable difference between them & the English Natives. If the English live past 33 they generally live to a good age; but many die between 30 & 33.

21.　　I have been told that one of their famous Wiochists prophcyed that bearded men <for the American Indians have no beards> should come & take away their Country & that there should none of the original Indians be left, within a certain number of years. I think it was an hundred & fifty. This is very certain that the Indian inhabitants of Virginia are now very inconsiderable as to their number; & seem insensibly to decay though they live under the English protection & have no violence offered them. They are undoubtedly no great breeders.

22.　　Though they are sluggish by nature & slow of speech, yet their method of expression seems vehement & Emphatical & allways atended with strong gesticulations. They are generally well proportioned & for the most part are rather taller than the English. They have all either a very dark brown hair, that may well be called black; or a jett black all lank.

To 23, 24, I can give you no satisfactory answer. They are to me OCULTA ARCANA.[58]

[58] Mysterious secrets (?).

V

"THE AIR AND
TEMPERATURE . . . IS MUCH
GOVERN'D BY WINDS
IN VIRGINIA"

A Letter from Mr. John Clayton Rector of Crofton at Wakefield in Yorkshire to the Royal Society, May 12, 1688, giving an Account of several Observables in Virginia, and in his Voyage thither, more particularly concerning the Air.[1]

Having often times been urged to give an Account of *Virginia* by several of the worthy Members of the Royal Society, I cannot but, as far forth as I am able, obey Commands whereby I'm so much honour'd, and show my Respect by my ready Compliance; tho' I am so sensible of my own Weakness and Incapacity to answer your Expectations, that before-hand I must Apologize for my self. And indeed by Sea I lost all my Books, Chymical Instruments, Glasses and Microscopes, which rendered me uncapable of making those Remarks and Observations I had designed, they were all cast away in Captain *Wins* ship,[2] as they were to follow me; and Virginia being a

---

[1] The originals of these letters on Virginia do not seem to have survived. This is taken from *Phil. Trans.*, XVII (1693), 781–89.

[2] There are many references to Captain John Wynne in the letters of William Byrd I. Writing Mr. North, April 26, 1684, he mentions "those goods you Sent me by Wynne." He adds that Wynne "reckons to saile about the last of next Month." Wynne left Virginia some time after May 20, for Byrd wrote to Perry & Lane on that date, saying, "This accompany Capt Wynne with four Hds of ffurres" (Stanard, "Letters of William Byrd, First," pp. 229–30). Either Wynne merely had an interest in the ship which was to bring Clayton's baggage or he survived the shipwreck, for he appears in later letters.

Country where one cannot furnish ones self again with such things, I was discourag'd from making so diligent a Scruteny as otherwise I might have done, so that I took very few Minutes down in Writing; and therefore, since I have only my Memory to rely on, which too has the Disadvantage of it's own Weakness, and of the distance of two years since now I left the Country, if future Relations shall in some small Points make out my Mistake, I thought this requisite to justifie my Candor; for I ever judg'd it villanous to impose in matters of Fact; but Descriptions of things that depend on memory may be liable to Mistakes, and yet the Sincerity of the Person that delivers them intire. But hereof I shall be as cautious as possible, and shall rather wave some things whereof I have some Doubts, and am uncapable now of satisfying my self, than in any sort presume too far. The Method I design is, First, to give an Account of the Air, and all such Observations as refer thereto, then of the Water, the Earth and Soil; the Birds, the Beasts, the Fishes, the Plants, the Insects; and lastly, the present state of the Inhabitants: But at present I shall neither trouble you nor my self with any more than an Account of what refers to the Air alone, being conscious the Honourable Society may receive such a Glut with the Imperfection of this, as to excuse me from a farther Relation.

But before I begin, perhaps it may not be impertinent to acquaint you with some things that happen'd in our Voyage. We Sail'd in the Ship *Judith,* Captain *Trim* Commander, 'twas Fly-boat built,[3] about 200 or 250 Tuns; she sprung a considerable Leak. When the Captain had made long and diligent Search, had tried all Methods that Sea-men use upon such occasions, or he could think of all in vain, and that the Leak

[3] Nothing has been learned concerning the "Judith" or Captain Trim. "Fly-boat built" merely indicated a speedy craft, which might be of several types.

encreased, he came pensively to consult me. Discoursing with him about it, and understanding that the Ship was Seeled within; so that though the Leak might possibly be in the forepart, it would fill the whole Cavity betwixt the Seeling and the Planks, and so run into the Hold at all the Crevices of the Seeling up and down. I thereupon conceived, that where it burst in betwixt the Seeling and the Planks, it must needs make some Noise. He told me, they had endeavoured to find it out that way, and according to custom had clapt Cans to their Ears to hear with; but the working of the Ship, the Tackle and the Sea made such a noise, that they could discover nothing thereby, I happily bethought my self of the Speaking Trumpet; and having one which I had contrived for some other Conveniences, of a differing shape from the common sorts, I bid him take it and apply the broad end to the side of the Ship, the narrow end to his Ear, and it would encrease his Hearing as much as it augmented the Voice the other way, and would ward the Ear too from the Confusion of Foreign Noise. Upon the first application, accordingly they heard it, tho' it happen'd to be at a considerable distance; and when they removed the Trumpet nigher, they heard it as if it had been the Current of a mighty River, even so distinctly, as to have Apprehensions of the bigness and Figure of the Hole that the Water came in at; so that cutting there the Seeling of the Ship, they immediately stopt the Leak.

In the Sea I saw many little things which the Seamen call Carvels; they are like a Jelly or Starch that is made with a Cast of Blew in it; they swim like a small Sheeps Bladder above the Water, downwards there are long fibrous strings, some whereof I have found near half a yard long.[4] This I take to be a

---

[4] Portuguese man-of-war (one of the species of the genus *Physalia*). The bladder, extending partly above the surface of the water, caused the sailors to name them after the caravel, or carvels, a small sailing ship with a high stern

sort of Sea-Plant, and the strings its Roots growing in the Sea, as Duck-weed[5] does in Ponds. It may be reckon'd among the Potential Cauteries;[6] for when we were one day becalm'd, getting some to make Observations thereof, the sportful People rub'd it on one anothers Hands and Faces, and where it touch'd it would make it look very red, and make it smart worse than a Nettle. In my return for *England* we struck a Hauksbill Turtle,[7] in whose Guts I found many of these Carvels; so that it's manifest they feed thereon. 'Tis commonly asserted by the Seamen, that they can smell the Pines at *Virginia* several Leagues at Sea before they see Land, but I could receive no satisfaction as to this Point; I could not discern any such thing when at a moderate distance, I fear much of this may be attributed to Fancy; for one day there came three or four full [fools] sent to tell me they were certain they smelt the Pines, but it afterwards prov'd that we were at that time 200 Leagues from the Shoar, so that I was satisfied that was therefore meer Fancy. Indeed we thought, by the general Accounts of the Ship, that we had been just on the Coast, but all were deceived by a Current we met with,[8] that at

---

and a lateen sail. *Physalia* species, although preferring warm waters, have sometimes been found in the Gulf Stream as far north as England. Clayton was mistaken in believing them plants, a belief commonly held in his day.

[5] Small, free-floating members of the family Lemnaceae.

[6] Not used in the modern sense, but rather as a counter-irritant, possibly to induce improved circulation.

[7] *Eretmochelys imbricata* of the order Chelonia. Tortoise-shell is supplied by this common inhabitant of the Atlantic, Pacific, and Indian Oceans, whose snout is a horny beak.

[8] For four centuries the Gulf Stream was thought to be one vast river. Clayton's commentary is particularly interesting because scientists have recently suggested that this current is four narrow streams, rather than one broad one. Between these are countercurrents, and the result is that the pattern of southwest to northeast flow of the Gulf Stream is often broken at points. Then it behaves, or appears to behave, much as Clayton described it, a current of "mischievous Consequence."

that time set about South-East, or East South-East, which when
once becalmed we tried thus: We hoisted out a Boat, and took
one of the Scuttles that cover'd one of the Hatches of the Ship,
tying thereto a great Weight, and a strong long Rope, we let it
sink a considerably [*sic*] Depth, and then fastning it to the
Boat, it serv'd as an Ancor, that the Boat could not drive; then
with the Glass and logg Line we found the Current set, as I say,
Eastward, at the rate of a Mile and a half an hour. This
Current is of mischievous Consequence, it does not always run
one way, but as it sets sometimes as we proved Easterly, so does
it, as they say, set at other times Westerly, whereby many Ships
have been lost; for then the Ships being before their Accounts,
they fall in with the Land before they are aware. Thus one
year many Ships were lost on Cape *Hattarasse,* and thereabouts.

OF THE AIRE.

The Cape called *Cape Henry,* lies in 36½ of the Northern
Latitude.[9] The Air and Temperature of the Seasons is much
govern'd by Winds in *Virginia,* both as to Heat and Cold,
Driness and Moisture, whose Variations being very notable, I
the more lamented the loss of my Barometers and Thermometers, for considerable Observations might be made thereby,
there being often great and suddain Changes. The Nore and
Nore-West are very nitrous and piercing, cold and clear, or else
stormy. The South-East and South hazy and soultry hot:
Their Winter is a fine clear Air, and dry, which renders it very
pleasant: Their Frosts are short, but sometimes very sharp,
that it will freeze the Rivers over three miles broad; nay, the
Secretary of State[10] assured me, it had frozen clever [*sic*] over

[9] It is nearer 37+ than 36½ degrees latitude. Cape Henry and Cape
Charles mark the entrance of Chesapeake Bay in Virginia.
[10] Spencer.

Potomack River, over against his House, where it is near nine Miles over, I have observed it freezes there the hardest, when from a moist South East, on a suddain the Wind passing by the Nore, a nitrous sharp Nore-West blows; not with high Gusts but with a cutting brisk Air; and those Vails then that seem to be shelter'd from the Wind, and lie warm, where the Air is most stagnant and moist, are frozen the hardest, and seized the soonest, and there the Fruits are more subject to blast than where the Air has a free Motion.   Snow falls sometimes in pretty quantity, but rarely continues there above a day or two: Their Spring is about a Month earlier than in *England;* in *April* they have frequent Rains, sometimes several short and suddain Gusts. *May* and *June* the Heat encreases, and it is much like our Summer, being mitigated with gentle Breezes, that rise about Nine of the Clock, and decrease and incline as the Sun rises and falls. *July* and *August* those Breezes cease, and the Air becomes stagnant, that the Heat is violent and troublesom.   In *September* the Weather usually breaks suddenly, and there falls generally very considerable Rains. When the Weather breaks many fall sick, this being the time of an Endemical Sickness, for Seasonings, Cachexes, Fluxes, Scorbutical Dropsies, Gripes or the like, which I have attributed to this Reason.[11]   That by the extraordinary Heat the Ferment of the Blood being raised too high, and the Tone of the Stomach relaxed, when the Weather breaks the Blood palls, and like over-fermented Liquors is depauperated, or turns eager and sharp, and there's a crude Digestion, whence the named Distempers may be supposed to ensue.   And for Confirmation, I have observed the Carminative Seeds,[12] such as warm, and whose Oil sheaths the acid Humours that ever result from crude Digestions.   But Decoctions that retain the Tone of the

[11] See p. 26, n. 13.
[12] "Carminative," related to the expelling of gas from the digestive system.

Stomach, as I suppose, by making the little Glands in the Tunicles[13] of the Stomach, squeeze out their Juice, <for what is bitter may be as well offensive to the Stomach, as to the Palat> and then Chalibiates[14] that raise the decayed Ferment, are no bad Practice; after which, I conceive, Armoniack Spirits[15] might be very beneficial. But their Doctors are so Learned, that I never met with any of them that understood what Armoniack Spirits were: Two or three of them one time ran me clear down by consent, that they were vomitive, and that they never used any thing for that purpose but Crocus Metallorum,[16] which indeed every House keeps; and if their Finger, as the Saying is, ake but, they immediately give three or four spoonfuls thereof; if this fail, they give him a second Dose, then perhaps purge them with 15 or 20 Grains of the Rosin of Jalap,[17] afterwards sweat them with Venice Treacle,[18] Powder of Snake-Root,[19] or *Gascoins* Powder;[20] and when these fail *con-*

---

[13] Membrane lining the stomach.

[14] Permeated with salts of iron; thus, chalybeate springs.

[15] Spirits of ammonia.

[16] A metallic oxide, especially colcothar, an oxide of iron.

[17] Still widely used. A very strong purgative derived from the plant, *Exogonium purga* (Wenderoth) Bentham, once extensively cultivated near Jalapa, Mexico, and exported to the United States.

[18] Theriaca andromachi, various drugs combined in a paste and prepared with honey.

[19] Possibly Virginia snakeroot (*Aristolochia serpentaria* L.), now used as an aromatic bitter. The term "snakeroot" has been applied to a number of plants.

[20] A powder composed of one pound of compound powder of crab's claws mixed with one ounce of prepared Oriental bezoar. Bezoar is a stone found in the intestine of various land animals, e.g., the ox, the Alpine goat, the gazelle and the porcupine. Oriental bezoar is found in the fourth stomach of *Capra aegagrus* of the Persian mountains. This information was kindly sent to us by the librarian of the Royal College of Surgeons in Ireland. John Houghton wrote of Gascoin's powder in 1696: "an excellent medicine indeed, and in very great use with our English physicians" (*A Collection of Letters for the Improvement of Husbandry and Trade*, rev. by Richard Bradley [London, 1727], II [July 10, 1696], 68).

clamatum est.[21]   But to return, 'Tis wonderful what Influence the Air has over Mens Bodies, whereof I had my self sad Assurances; for tho' I was in a very close warm Room, where was a Fire constantly kept, yet there was not the least Alteration or Change, whereof I was not sensible when I was sick of the Gripes, of which Distemper I may give a farther account in it's proper place.   When a very ingenious Gentlewoman was visited with the same Distemper, I had the opportunity of making very considerable Observations.   I stood at the Window, and could view the Clouds arise; For there small black fleeting Clouds will arise, and be swiftly carry'd cross the whole Element; and as these Clouds arose, and came nigher, her Torments were encreased, which were grievous as a labouring Womans; there was not the least Cloud but lamentably affected her, and that at a considerable distance; but by her Shrieks it seemed more or less, according to the bigness and nearness of the Clouds.   The Thunder there is attended often with fatal circumstances: I was with my Lord *Howard* of *Effingham* the Governour,[22] when they brought word that one Dr. A. was killed therewith, after this manner: He was smoaking a Pipe of Tobacco, and looking out at his Window when he was struck dead, and immediately became so stiff, that he did not fall, but stood leaning in the Window, with the Pipe in his mouth in the same posture he was in when struck: But this I only deliver as Report, tho' I heard the same Account from several, without any contradicting it. These things are remarkable, that it generally breaks in at the Gable end of the Houses, and often kills Persons in, or near the Chimneys Range, darting most fiercely down the Funnel of the Chimney, more especially if there be a Fire, <I speak here confusedly of Thunder and Lightning> for when they do any Mischief, the Crash and Lightning are at the same instant, which must be from the

[21] "It is bewailed."   [22] See p. xxx.

nearness of the Cloud.   One time when the Thunder split the Mast of a Boat at *James* Town, I saw it break from the Cloud, which it divided in two, and seem'd as if it had shot them immediately a Mile asunder, to the Eye: It is dangerous when it Thunders standing in a narrow passage, where there's a thorough passage, or in a Room betwixt two Windows; tho' several have been kill'd in the open Fields.   'Tis incredible to tell how, it will strike large Oaks, shatter and shiver them, sometimes twisting round a Tree, sometimes as if it struck the Tree backwards and forwards. I had noted a fine spreading Oak in *James Town* Island, in the Morning I saw it fair and flourishing, in the Evening I observed all the Bark of the Body of the Tree, as if it had been artificially peel'd off, was orderly spread round the Tree in a Ring, whose Semidiameter was Four Yards, the Tree in in [*sic*] the Center; all the Body of the Tree was shaken and split, but its Boughs had all their Bark on; few Leaves were fallen, and those on the Boughs as fresh as in the Morning, but gradually afterwards withered, as on a Tree that is fallen.   I have seen several vast Oaks and other Timber Trees twisted, as if it had been a small Willow that a Man had twisted with his Hand, which I could suppose had been done by nothing but the Thunder.   I have been told by very serious Planters, that 30 or 40 years since, when the Country was not so open, the Thunder was more fierce, and that sometimes after violent Thunder and Rains, the Roads would seem to have perfect casts of Brimstone;[23] and 'tis frequent after much Thunder and Lightning for the Air to have a perfect Sulphureous Smell.   Durst I offer my weak Reasons when I write to so great Masters thereof, I should here consider the nature of Thunder, and compare it with some Sulphureous Spirits which I have drawn from Coals, that I

[23] "Brimstone" was an old term for sulphur.

could no way condense, yet were inflamable;[24] nay, would burn after they pass'd through Water, and that seemingly fiercer, if they were not over-power'd therewith. I have kept of this Spirit a considerable time in Bladders; and tho' it appeared as if they were only blown with Air, yet if I let it forth, and fired it with a Match or Candle, it would continue burning till all were spent. It might be worthy Consideration likewise, whether those frequent Thunders proceeded from the Air's being more stagnant, the Motion of the Winds being impeded by the Trees, or whether the Motion of the Winds being obstructed by them below, the Motion might not be more violent aloft; and how far that may promote Inflammability, for Stacks of Hay or Corn that ferment with Moisture, never burn, unless when brisk Winds blow, that agitate and fan the little fermenting Sparks, and oft kindle them into an actual Fire.[25] An Observance of the Meteors there might perhaps not be impertinent, as both what are more rare, and what are more frequent, as of *Gosimore*[26] in great abundance, and of those small Cobwebs in a Morning, which some have supposed to be Meteors, *Ignes fatui,*[27] tho' there be many boggy Swamps and Marshes, are seldom, if any are seen there. There be frequent little sorts of Whirl-winds, whose Diameter may be sometimes not past two or three Yards, sometimes Forty, which whisking round in a Circle, pass along the Earth, according to the Motion of the Cloud, from whence they issue; and as they pass along with their gyrous or circular Motion, they carry aloft the

[24] See account of Clayton's experiments with the spirit of coals on pp. 138–40.

[25] Spontaneous combustion.

[26] Webster calls gossamer a cloud of cobwebs "floating in the air in calm clear weather."

[27] Flickering lights over marshes, thought to be caused by methane combustion.

drie Leaves into the Air, which fall again often in places far remote. I have seen them descend in a calm Sun-shine Day, as if they had come from the Heavens in great Showers thereof, so that all the Elements seem'd filled therewith. And I could perceive them to descend from on high as far as I could possibly discern a Leaf. I remember a roguish Expression of a Seaman, otherwise silly enough, who wondering thereat, cry'd out, *Sure now 'tis manifest there is a World above!* and now with them 'tis the fall of the Leaf. But to proceed, I thought this made it manifest, whence many preternatural Showers have happen'd. I remember at Sir *Richard Atherton's* in *Lancashire,*[28] some few years ago, there fell a great number of the Seeds of Ivy-berries;[29] at first we admir'd what they were, for they were cover'd with a thin skin that was red, and resembled the Figure of a small Wheat Corn; but afterwards they fully manifested what they were; for many sprouted and took Root. I suppose they were carry'd aloft by some such Whirl-wind, and let fall there. I have purposely gone into the place where I perceiv'd this Gust, which is notorious enough by the noise it makes, with ratling the Leaves as it carries them aloft, and have found a fine sharp Breeze of Wind. *Yours etc.*

[28] Clayton's first cousin on his mother's side.
[29] Probably seeds of *Hedera helix,* English ivy.

VI

"WATERS IN THE
SPRINGS . . . ARE . . . MORE EAGER
THAN THOSE IN ENGLAND"

Mr. Clayton's Second Letter, containing his farther Observations on Virginia.[1]

Being honour'd with the Thanks of the Society for my last, and receiving by my worthy Friend Dr. *Moulin*[2] their Commands to proceed, I have added here my Observations of the Waters, and part of the Earth and Soil. I shall wave both Complements and Apologies, since I have greater Respect and Honour for the Society than I can possibly express, and have no reason to suspect their Favour, whose Candidness I so signally proved in my last.

OF THE WATERS.

Twixt the two Capes, the Southern, call'd the *Cape Henry,* the more Northerly call'd *Cape Charles,* there runs up a great Bay, call'd the Bay of *Cheesepeak;* Nine Leagues over in some places, in most Seven, lying much West, Nore and South, dividing *Virginia* into two unequal parts. On the East side of this Bay there lies a narrow Neck of Land, which makes the Counties of *Northampton* and *Accomack.* On the West side of the Bay there branches forth four great Rivers, *James River,*

---

[1] This must have been read in June or July 1688. It was printed in two parts in *Phil. Trans.,* XVII (1693), 790–95, 941–48. The original does not seem to have survived.

[2] Allen Moulin, M.D., F.R.S. See pp. xxxix–xli.

York River, Rapahanack and *Potomack,* that rise from a Ridge of Mountains, whereof more in the Sequel. These Rivers plentifully water all the other parts of *Virginia,* emptying themselves into the great Bay. The Mouth of *James River,* which is the most Southerly of them, to the Mouth of *Potomack,* which is the most Northerly, may be a hundred Miles distance: But as I have been credibly inform'd, that the Falls of *James River* are not past Thirty Miles from *Potomack,* which is a vast large River Nine Miles over in many places. I have been told it was Navigable nigh Two Hundred Miles, much higher than any of the other Rivers: Whence I conclude in future times, it will be the most considerable for Trade when the Country comes to be inhabited further up into the main Land. The other Rivers are much about Three Miles over apiece. And *James River* is Navigable at least Eighty Miles. Within Four or Five Miles of *James Town,* *James River* and *York River* are not past Four or Five Miles asunder. Yea, Sloops of considerable Carriage may Sail up the Branches of the two Rivers, till they come within a Mile the one of the other; for I take it to be no more from Col. *Bollard's*[3] to Major *Troop's*[4] Landing; and I believe they may come much what as near again as Col. *Coles,*[5] and several other places. *York River* is distant from *Rapahanack* in some places not past Ten or Twelve Miles, *Rapahanack* from *Potomack* not past Seven Miles in one place, tho' it may be Sixty in others. The Heads of the Branches of the Rivers interfere and lock one within another, which I think is best expressed after the manner that an *Indian* explained himself once to me, when I enquired how nigh the Rivers of *Carolina, Virginia* and

---

[3] Probably refers to Colonel Thomas Ballard, a member of the Council.

[4] Major Troop remains unidentified.

[5] This should probably read "*at* Col. Coles." The reference may be to William Cole, of Warwick County, member of the Council.

Maryland arose out of the Mountains, from those that ran Westerly on the other side of the Mountains, he clapt the Fingers of one Hand 'twixt those of the other, crying, they meet thus; the Branches of different Rivers rising not past a hundred Paces distant one from another: So that no Country in the World can be more curiously watered. But this Conveniency, that in future times may make her like the *Netherlands* the richest place in all *America,* at the present I look on the greatest Impediment to the Advance of the Country, as it is the greatest Obstacle to Trade and Commerce. For the great number of Rivers and the thinness of the Inhabitants distract and disperse a Trade. So that all Ships in general gather each their Loading up and down an hundred Miles distant; and the best of Trade that can be driven is only a sort of *Scotch* Pedling; for they must carry all sort of Truck that trade thither, having one Commodity to pass off another. This <i.e.> the number of Rivers, is one of the chief Reasons why they have no Towns; for every one being more sollicitous for a private Interest and Conveniency, than for a publick, they will either be for making Forty Towns at once, that is, two in every County, or none at all, which is the Countries Ruine. But to return, The Tides in these Rivers regularly ebb and flow about two foot perpendicular at *James Town;* there is there, as they call it, a Tide and half Tide, that is, it flows near two hours along by the Shoar, after that it is Ebb in the Channel, and again it ebbs near two Hours by the Shore, after that it is Flood in the Channel. This is great advantage to the Boats passing up and down the River. I suppose this is caused by many Creeks and Branches of the Rivers, which being considerable many, tho' only three or four Miles long, yet as broad as the *Thames* at *London;* others Ten Miles long, some above Twenty, that have little fresh Water which they carry of their own, but their Current primarily depending upon the Flux and Reflux of the Sea. So that after the Tide is made in the Channel, it flows by the Shoar a considerable time afterwards, being that those Creeks are still to fill, and therefore as it were draws a Source upwards by the Shoar; and likewise when the Tide returns in the Channel, the Creeks that could not so readily disburse their Water, being still to empty themselves, they make an ebbing by the Shoar a considerable time after that it is Flood, as I say, in the Channel. So far as the Salt Waters reach the Country is deemed less healthy. In the Freshes they more rarely are troubled with the Seasonings, and those Endemical Distempers about *September* and *October*. This being very remarkable, I refer the Reason to the more piercing Genius of those most judicious Members of the Society; And it might perhaps be worthy the Disquisition of the Most Learned to give an Account of the various Alterations and fatal Effects that the Air has on humane Bodies, especially when impregnated with a Marine Salt: more peculiarly when such an Air becomes stagnant: This might perhaps make several beneficial Discoveries, not only in relation to those Distempers in *America,* but perhaps take in your *Kentish* Agues, and many others remarkable enough in our own Nation. I lately was making some Observations of this Nature on a Lady of delicate Constitution, who living in a clear Air, and removing towards the Sea-Coast, was lamentably afflicted therewith, which both my self and others attributed to this Cause, she having formerly upon her going to the same been seized in the same manner. But to return: There is one thing more in reference to this very thing very remarkable in *Virginia,* generally twice in the year, Spring and Fall, at certain Spring Tides, the most of the Cattle will set on gadding, and run, tho' it be twenty or thirty Miles, to the River to drink the Salt Water, at which time there's scarce any stopping of them; which the People know so well, that if about those times their Heards are stray'd from their Plantations, without more solicitation they go directly to the Rivers to fetch them home again. As for the Waters in the Springs in general, they are, I think, somewhat more eager than those in *England*. In that I have observed, they require some quantity more of Mault to make strong Beer than our English Waters, and will not bear Soap. I have try'd several by infusing of Galls,[6] and found little difference in the Colours, turning much what the Colour of common Sack[7] in Taverns. I tried two Wells at Col. *Bird's,* by the Falls of *James River,* several Wells near *James Town,* some Springs in the *Isle of Wight County:* There's a Spring in the *Isle of Wight* or *Nanzamond County* vents the greatest Source of Water I ever saw, excepting *Holy Well* in *Wales,* but I had not the opportunity to make experiments thereof. I tried likewise some Springs on the Banks of *York River,* in *New Kent* and *Gloucester County,* but found them vary very little as to Colour. I could not trie any thing as to their specifick Gravity, having neither Aquapoise,[8] nor those other Glasses I had contrived peculiarly for making such Experiments, they being all lost with my other things. I had Glasses blown would hold about Five Ounces, others about Ten Ounces, with Necks so small, that a Drop would make a considerable Variation; with these I could make much more critical and satisfactory Observations as to the specifical Gravity of Liquors, having Critical Scales, than by any other way yet by me tried. I used this method to weigh Urines,[9] which Practice I would recommend to the inquisitive and critical

[6] Infusions of oak galls were widely used in testing waters for mineral salts. The infusion turned black in the presence of iron. The test dates back to the time of Paracelsus (1493–1541), according to Gunther, *Early Science,* II, 13–14.

[7] Sack was any of various strong white wines of southern Europe.

[8] An instrument for weighing a substance in water.

[9] This diagnostic method is used today. In the seventeenth century the medical profession placed great stress on urinalysis as a means of mystifying their patients and generally impressing them. Blanton emphasizes that Clayton was "not a uroscopist or urine gazer of the ordinary variety" (*Medicine in Virginia,* p. 142).

Physicians. I had made many Observations hereof, but all
Notes were likewise lost with my other things. Yet I have
begun afresh; for there are more signal Variations in the
Weights of Urines, than one would at first imagine; and when
the Eye can discover little, but judge two Urines to be alike,
they may be found to differ very much as to Weight. By
Weight I find Observations may be made of Affections in the
Head, which rarely make any visible Alterations in the
Urine. I have found two Urines not much unlike differ two
and twenty Grains in the quantity of about four or five
Ounces: But let them that make these Essays weigh all their
Urines when cold, lest they be thereby deceiv'd. But to return
to the Spring Waters in *Virginia*. There's a Spring at my
Lady *Berkeley's*[10] called *Green-Spring,* whereof I have been
often told, so very cold, that 'tis dangerous drinking thereof in
Summer-time, it having proved of fatal Consequence to sev-
eral. I never tried any thing of what nature it is of.

   There be many petrefying Waters; and indeed I believe few
of the Waters but participate of a petrefying quality, tho' there
be few Pebbles or paving Stones to be found in all the
Country. But I have found many Sticks with crusty Congela-
tions[11] round them in the Runs of Springs, and Stones figured
like Honey-Combs, with many little Stars as it were shot in the
Holes.[12] And nothing is more common than petrefy'd Shells,
unless you would determine that they are parts of natural
Rock shot in those Figures, which indeed I rather think; but
thereof hereafter. Mr. Secretary *Spencer* has told me of some
Waters participating much of *Alome,*[13] or *Vitriol*[14] towards

   [10] The widow of Sir William Berkeley, who had named his plantation for
this spring. His land was located three miles from Jamestown.
   [11] Crystalline deposits.
   [12] Possibly coral.
   [13] Potassium aluminum sulphate.
   [14] The term "vitriol" is applied to the sulphates of various metals.

Potomack. Up beyond the Falls of *Rapahanack* I have heard of Poysonous Waters. But these I only mention as a Hint to further Enquiry of some others, for I can say nothing of them my self.[15]

When you make the Capes of *Virginia*, you may observe it low Land, so that at some distance the Trees appear as if they grew in the Water; and as you approach nigher, to emerge thence. For a hundred Miles up into the Country, there are few Stones to be found, only in some places, Rocks of Iron Oar appear,[16] which made me expect to have found many Waters turn Purple with Galls, but never met with any. Providence has supplied the common use of Stones, by making the Roads very good: so that they ride their Horses without shooing them; which yet are more rarely beaten on their Feet, than ours are in *England*, the Country and Clime being dry, their Hoofs are much harder: for I observed, that take a Horse out of the wet Marshes, and Swamps, as they there call them, and ride him immediately, and he'll quickly be tender-footed. In some places, for several Miles together, the Earth is so inter-mix'd with Oyster-shells, that there may seem as many Shells as Earth: and how deep they lie thus intermingled, I think, is not yet known: for at broken Banks they discover themselves to be continued many Yards perpendicular. In several places these Shells are much closer, and being petrefied, seem to make a Vein of a Rock. I have seen in several places, Veins of these

[15] It is rather surprising that Clayton makes no mention of springs containing sulphur. At this point the first section of the printed version ends with the words: "The remainder of this Letter being his Observations on the Earth and Soil of Virginia shall be reserved for the next Transaction."

[16] Iron deposits were a prime concern of the Jamestown settlers. Captain John Smith sent samples of ore to England as early as 1608. For an interesting account of early attempts to exploit Virginia's iron deposits, see C. E. Hatch, Jr., and T. G. Gregory, "The First American Blast Furnace, 1619–1622," *Va. Mag. Hist. Biog.*, LXX (1962), 259–96.

Rocky Shells, three or four Yards thick, at the foot of a Hill, whose precipice might be twenty Yards perpendicular, whose Delf,[17] I suppose, shot under the Hill, pieces of these Rocks broken off, lie there, which, I suppose, may weigh twenty or thirty Tuns a piece, and are as difficult to be broken as our Free-stone.[18] Of these Rocks of Oyster-shells that are not so much petrefied, they burn and make all their Lime;[19] whereof they have that store, that no Generation will consume. Whether these were formerly Oysters, which left by the subsiding Seas, <as some suppose, that all that Tract of Land, now high Ground, was once overflowed by the Sea> were since petrefied, or truly Stones, *Sui Generis,* I leave to the Honourable Society to determine. But when I consider the constant and distinct shooting of several Salts,[20] Nature's Curiosity, in every thing, so far exceeding that of Art, that the most Ingenious, when referr'd thereto, seem only endued with an Apish fondness, I cannot think any thing too difficult or wonderful for Nature; and indeed, I do not apprehend, why it may not be as feasible to suppose them to have been Rocks, at first shot into those Figures, as to conceive the Sea to have amass'd such a vast Number of Oyster-shells one upon another, and afterwards subsiding, should leave them cover'd with such Mountains of Earth, under which they should petrefie: But not to launch forth too far into those Disputes, since I must modestly

[17] That which may be delved into – as a bed of any earth or mineral.

[18] Limestone or sandstone.

[19] These deposits of oyster shells seem to have amazed the colonists and visitors to the Colonies. One early report of their use in mortar was made by Thomas Glover, "An Account of Virginia," *Phil. Trans.,* XI (1676), 623–36. See also Worth Bailey, "Lime Preparation at Jamestown in the Seventeenth Century," *William and Mary Quarterly,* ser. 2, XVIII (1938), 1–12.

[20] "Shooting of several Salts" probably refers to the formation of characteristic crystals by many chemical salts.

remember to whom I write.[21]   Often, in the looser Banks of
Shells and Earth, are found perfect Teeth petrefied, some
whereof I have seen, could not be less than two or three Inches
long, and above an Inch broad: Tho' they were not Maxilary
Teeth, the part that one might suppose grew out of the Jaw,
was polish'd, and black, almost as Jett; the part which had
been fasten'd in the Jaw and Gums, was brown, and not so
shiningly polish'd, or smooth; if they were, as they seemed to
be, really Teeth, I suppose, they must have been of Fishes.[22]
The Back-bone of a Whale, and as I remember, they told me of
some of the Ribs, were digg'd out of the side of a Hill, several
Yards deep in the Ground, about four Miles distant from
James-Town, and the River.   Mr. *Banister,*[23] a Gentleman
pretty curious in those things, shew'd me likewise the Joynt of
a Whale's Back-bone, and several Teeth, some whereof, he
said, were found in Hills beyond the Falls of *James* River, at
least, a Hundred and fifty Miles up into the Country.   The
Soyl in general is sandy: I had designed, and I think it might
be worth a Critical Remark, to observe, the Difference of Soyls
seem appropriated to the several sorts of Tobacco: for there is
not only the two distinct sorts of a Sweet-scented, and Aranoko
Tobacco,[24] but of each of these be several sorts much different,

[21] Clayton seems to have advanced the concept of inorganic evolution de-
liberately – a concept evidently believed by others in Virginia – and to have
carefully provided himself with a line of retreat in case the august members
of the Society disapproved.

[22] These were probably sharks' teeth.

[23] See pp. xxxi–xxxii.

[24] "Aranoko" referred to *Nicotiana tabacum,* introduced from the Orinoco
River Valley, in preference to *Nicotiana rustica,* the native species (N. M.
Tilley, *The Bright Tobacco Industry* [Chapel Hill, N.C., 1948], p. 5).   When
the English first arrived in Virginia, the Indians were smoking pipes of the
native tobacco, more for religious or ceremonial reasons than for pleasure,
according to B. C. McCary (*Indians in Seventeenth-Century Virginia*
[Williamsburg, Va., 1957], pp. 23–24).

the Seeds whereof are known by distinct Names, they having
given them the Names of those Gentlemen most famed for
such sort of Tobacco, as of *Prior*-seed, etc.[25] Nay, the same sort
of Seed in different Earths, will produce Tobacco much different, as to goodness. The richer the Ground, the better it is for
Aranoko Tobacco,[26] whose Scent is not much minded, their
only aim being to have it specious, large, and to procure it a
bright Kite's-foot colour.[27] Had not my Microscopes, etc.
Tools to grind Glasses, been cast away, with my other things, I
had made some Critical Enquiries into their several Natures, I
would have examin'd what Proportions of Salts, all the sorts of
Earths had afforded, and how Water impregnated with their
Salts, would have changed with infusing Galls, how with the
Syrup of Violets, and how they would have precipitated Mercury, or the like, and so far forth as I had been able, examined
them by the several Tryals of Fire.[28] I conceive Tobacco to be
a Plant abounding with Nitro-Sulphurious Particles;[29] for the

[25] A variety of tobacco which is still known by the name of "Pryor," possibly
developed by the Virginia planter William Pryor, whose wife, Margaret
Clayton, was a distant relative of the minister. She was the sister of Sir Jasper
Clayton of London, great-grandfather of the botanist.

[26] Although Clayton, and probably others, recognized the sensitivity of tobacco to different soils at this time, yet "the beneficent effect of a lighter soil
on the sensitive tobacco plant confronted growers for many years before it
was cultivated in the siliceous soils of the Piedmont" (Tilley, *Bright Tobacco*,
p. 4).

[27] "Kite's-foot colour" was bright yellow (*ibid.*, p. 9).

[28] "Syrupus Violal, Syrup of Violet. Take of the fresh petals of violets lb
ii [2 lbs.], boiling distilled water three pints: macerate them for twenty
four hours; afterwards strain through a fine linen rag without expression,
and add the clarified sugar to make a syrup" (G. Mothery, M.D., *A New
Medical Dictionary* [4th ed.; London, 1795], p. 728). Robert Boyle showed
that "all common acids turned syrup of violets red, and that no substance apparently not an acid did so" (Marie Boas, *Robert Boyle and Seventeenth-
Century Chemistry* [Cambridge, 1958], p. 135). Precipitation of mercury
and "Tryals of Fire" were other chemical tests of the time.

[29] Both nitrogen and sulphur are essential elements for the normal growth
of tobacco, and both are present in the leaf, but not in any unusual quantity.

Planters try the goodness of their Seed, by casting a little thereof into the Fire; if it be good, it will sparkle after the manner of Gunpowder:[30] so will the Stalks of Tobacco-leaves, and perhaps has something analagous to the Narcotick Sulphur of *Venus*,[31] which the Chymists so industriously labour after. The World knows little of the efficacy of its Oyl, which has wonderful Effects in the curing of old inveterate Sores, and Scropulous Swellings, and some, otherwise applied and qualified.[32] The goodness of Tobacco I look on primarily consists in the volatility of its Nitre: And hence the sandy Grounds that are most impregnated therewith, and whose Nitrous Salt is most volatile, for such Grounds are quickliest spent, yield Tobacco's that have the richest Scent, and that shortly becomes a pleasant Smoak; whereas, in Tobacco that grows on stiff Ground, the Salts seem more fix'd, and lock'd up in the Oyl, so that whilst new, 'tis very heady and strong, and requires some time for its Salts to free themselves, and become volatile; which it manifests, by its having an Urinous Smell. The same Reason satisfies, why Tobacco that grows on low Lands as far as the Salts, tho' the Plant be never overflowed with Salt Water, yet the Ground that feeds the Plant being impregnated with Salt Water, that Tobacco smoaks not pleasantly, and will scarcely keep Fire, but do all that a Man can, will oft go out, and gives much trouble in frequent lighting

---

[30] Gunpowder is a mixture of saltpeter (potassium nitrate or sodium nitrate), charcoal, and sulphur.

[31] "Venus" was the alchemists' name for copper.

[32] In the sixteenth century canny Portuguese traders had encouraged a gullible public to accept tobacco as a medical cure-all, recommended in the treatment of fifty-nine diseases (J. E. Brooks, *The Mighty Leaf* [Boston, 1952], p. 40, and J. C. Robert, *The Story of Tobacco in America* [New York, 1949], p. 4). A whole chapter was devoted to tobacco and "his great vertues" by the Spanish physician, Nicholas Monardes, in his *Joyfull Newes Out of the New-found World*. This was the first book on New World botany and was translated into English in 1596.

the Pipe, 'till after it has been kept some considerable time: which may be assign'd to the fixeder Saline Particles of the Marine Salt in these Plants, which require more time e're they be render'd volatile. Here it might be worthy an Enquiry into the Nature of Filtration of Plants, since we may hence gather, Particles of the Marine Salt are carried along with the *Succus Nutritius* of the Plant; concerning which, if it were not too much to deviate from the Matter in hand, I should offer some Reflections of my own, which the Learned Society might perhaps improve: for I think thence might be made many happy Conjectures as to the Virtues of Plants, So where we see Plants, or Trees, of an open Pore growing low, we shall find their Juice has subtile parts: So have all Vines, whether the Grape Vine, or Briony,[33] or a Smilax, or the like. If a Gummous Plant or Tree, that grows low, and close pored, it abounds with acid Spirits, as *Lignum Vitae*,[34] etc. if it grow tall, and be open pored, it abounds with a subtile volatile Spirit, as your Firrs, and the Turpentine Tree. But to insist no further herein, than as this may be applicable to the present Discourse: for I have observed, that that which is called Pine-wood Land, tho' it be a sandy Soyl, even the Sweet-scented Tobacco that grows thereon, being large and porous, agreeable to Aranoko Tobacco: it smoaks as coursly as Aranoko: wherefore 'tis, that I believe the Microscope might make notable Discoveries towards the knowledge of good Tobacco: for the closer the Composition of the Leaf, the better the Tobacco: and therefore the Planters and Merchants brag of the Substance of their Tobacco; which word, did they always take it in a true sence, for the Solidness, and

[33] Briony or bryony (genus *Bryonia*), an herbaceous vine whose dried root is used as a cathartic.

[34] *Guaiacum officinale* L., a small tropical American tree with hard, heavy wood.

not mistake it for the Thickness, it would be more consonant to a true Observation:[35] for as I said of the Pine-wood Tobacco, some of it is thick and not solid, and differs from the Best Tobacco, as Buff does from Tann'd Leather; so that if the Tobacco be sound and not rotten, you may give a great guess at the goodness of Tobacco, when you weigh the Hogsheads, before you see them: for if an equal care be taken in the Packing of them, the best Tobacco will weigh the heaviest, and pack the closest. Now I said, that the Sweet-scented Tobacco most in vogue, which was most famed for its Scent, was that that grew on sandy Land; which is true, if you would smoak it whilst new, or whilst only two or three Years old; but if you keep the stiff Land Tobacco, which is generally a Tobacco of great Substance five or six Years, it will much excel: for tho' the sandy Land Tobacco abound with a volatile Nitre at first, yet the stiff Land Tobacco abounds with a greater quantity of Nitre, only that it is lock'd up in its Oyl at first, and requires more time to extricate itself, and become volatile; but the pine-wood Land having little of the Nitro-Sulphurious Particles, neither is, nor ever will make any thing of a rich Smoak.[36] Discoursing hereof some days since, to a Gentleman of good Observation, that has been versed with Maulting, he assured me, to back this my Supposition, or Hypothesis, he had observed, That Barly that grew on stiff Ground, required more

[35] This question seems to be still unsettled. "There is little experimental evidence bearing on variation in density of the tobacco leaf, but it has been suggested that a sustained low water content in the plant results in smaller, more compactly arranged leaf cells with smaller inter-cellular air spaces" (W. W. Garner, *The Production of Tobacco* [Philadelphia, 1951], p. 322).

[36] There is much variation in the length of time allowed for aging tobacco today, but apparently no variety is given as long a time as that suggested by Clayton. "Some tobaccos are well aged at the end of a year but 18 months to two years are usually needed and with some types two to three years are required" (*ibid.*, p. 423).

time considerably to mellow, and come to perfection, than that that grew in light Land. Having proceeded thus far to speak of Tobacco, I shall add one or two things more. The Planters differ in their Judgments about the Time of Planting, or Pitching their Crops: some are for Pitching their Crops very early, others late, without any distinction of the Nature of the Soyls;[37] and 'tis from the different Effects that they find, in that, sometimes early, sometimes the late Planting succeeds: but they have not the Reason to judge of the Cause, to consider the Accidents of the Year, and the Difference of the Soyls. In sandy Grounds they need not strive so much for early Planting, the looseness of the Earth, and the kind natured Soyl, yielding all that it can, easily and speedily, and Sand retaining the heat, makes the Plants grow faster. But in stiff Soyls, if the Crops be not early pitch'd, so that during the Season of Rains it have got considerable Roots, and shot them some depth, if early Droughts come, it so binds the Land, that the Roots never spread or shoot deeper, or further than the Hill that they are planted in: for they plant them as we do Cabbages, raising Hills to set every Plant in, about the bigness of a common Mole-hill:[38] observing this on the Plantation where I lived, that it was stiff Ground, I advised them to plant their Crops as early as possible; and in order thereunto, I tried several ways to further the Plants; but not to trouble you with the several Experiments that I made, in reference thereto: What I found most advantagious was, by taking an infusion of Horse-dung, and putting thereon Soot, and then my Seeds; this I kept Forty eight Hours in an ordinary digestive heat, I had two Beds left me to Sow, in the midst of those the People sow'd, and the

[37] This difference of opinion on the part of growers does not seem to have changed. "There is a rather wide variation in date of seeding the beds in any particular locality" (*ibid.*, p. 126).

[38] Ridging is still extensively, but not universally, practiced (*ibid.*, p. 130).

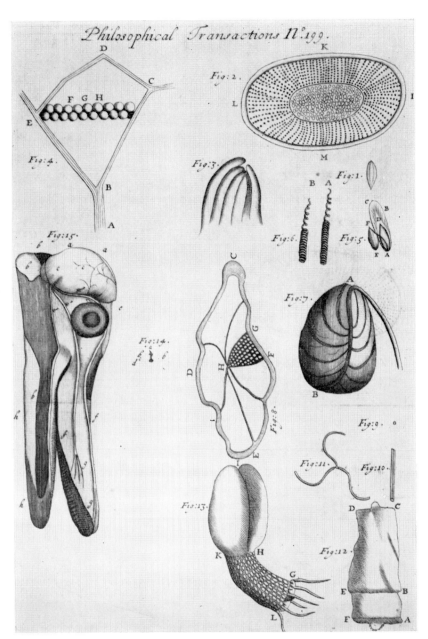

Philosophical Transactions N.° 199.

Plate III. Clayton's drawings for Moulin's article entitled "Anatomical Observations in the heads of Fowel made at several times," which appeared in *Philosophical Transactions*, XVII (1693), facing p. 693. The complete explanation of the plate does not seem to have survived, but Moulin gave the following explanation of Fig. 15: " (aa) Edge of Cranium; (bb) Cells about the Ear; (cc) the Brain; (dd) Nerves; (e) Optick Nerve; (fff) Skin and Part of Bone remov'd to bring the Nerve in View (gg) the two Nerves expanded near end of upper bill; (hh) lower bill." [See p. 95.] (Archives of the Royal Society of London)

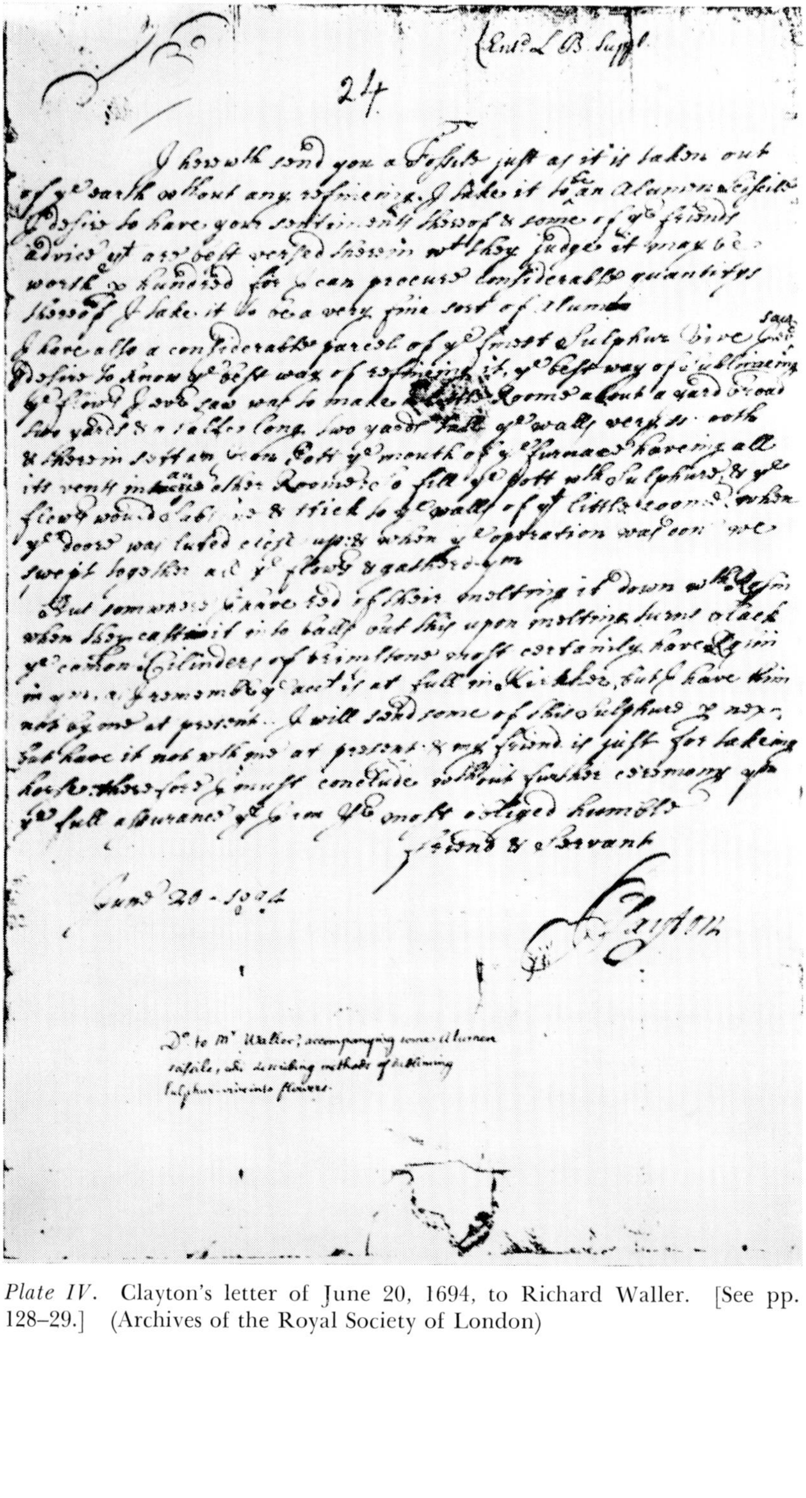

Plate IV. Clayton's letter of June 20, 1694, to Richard Waller. [See pp. 128–29.] (Archives of the Royal Society of London)

quantity of Seed that they generally allotted to the same quantity of Ground; when I sow'd, I mix'd Ashes with the Seed, having decanted the Liquor, that the Seed might sow the evenner:[39] the effect was, that my Plants came up much sooner, grew swifter, and I had five Plants for one more than any of the other Beds bore; I left the Country shortly after, and so had no certainty of the final Result. There be various Accidents and Distempers, whereunto Tobacco is liable, as the Worm, the Flie, Firing to Turn,[40] as they call them, French-men,[41] and the like. I proposed several ways to kill the Worm and Flie, as by Sulphur and the like; but had no opportunity to experiment it: I shall set down that I had most hopes of, which perhaps may give a hint to others to try or improve: Tobacco Seed is very small,[42] and by consequence so is the young Plant at first, that if gleamy Weather happen at that time, it breeds a small Flie, which consumes the Plume of the Plant; now it being

[39] Cabell, writing some time in the nineteenth century and referring to Clayton's method of (1) steeping the seed in an infusion of manure and (2) mixing it with ashes, said, "The first practice is still known to many planters and the last is universal" (N. F. Cabell, *Early History of Agriculture in Virginia* [Washington, 18–], p. 21). The dilution of the minute seeds to ensure even distribution when sowing is still routine today.

[40] The "Worm" probably referred to the southern hornworm or tomato worm (*Protoparce quinquemaculata* Haw.), still a very serious pest. The "Flie" may well have been the tobacco flea beetle, *Epitrix parvula* Fab., which also continues to be a problem. "Firing to Turn" has not been identified with any certainty. It may have been a fungous disease, such as Southern stem rot.

[41] Frenching is a disease known in all tobacco-raising regions of the world today. Clayton's description of it is particularly noteworthy. "Apparently frenching is the first tobacco disease to be clearly described. . . . The earliest account of frenching is contained in a letter, dated May 12, 1688, written by John Clayton, at Wakefield in Yorkshire, Va. [sic] and addressed to the Royal Society of England [sic]" (F. A. Wolf, *Tobacco Diseases and Decays* [Durham, N.C., 1957], p. 33). Wolf further notes (p. 44) that centuries of study of this disease have led to the apparent explanation of the cause as recently as 1951.

[42] Some 300,000 to 350,000 seeds per ounce, according to Garner (*Production of Tobacco*, p. 309).

early in the Year when they Sow the Seed, viz. about the 14th of *January*,[43] they cover the Ground, to secure, as well as they can, their tender Plants, from the nipping Frosts, that may happen in the Nights; they cover them only with a few Oak-leaves, or the like; for Straw they find apt to harbour and breed this Flie: I therefore would advise them to smoak Straw with Brimstone, once in two or three Nights, and so they might cover them securely, with that which would preserve them infinitely beyond the Covering with Oak-boughs;[44] indeed I would advise them to keep peculiarly so much of their *Indian* Corn-blades, which they gather for their Fodder, for this very purpose, being, as I conceive, much the best, there being no Chaff to foul their Beds, and prejudice them when they should weed them.   What they call Firing is this: When Plants are of small Substance as when there has been a very wet and cold Season, and very hot Weather suddenly ensues, the Leaves turn brown, and dry to dust; the Cause I conceive to be hence: The Plant being feeble, and having a small quantity of Oyl, which makes the more solid part of the Plant, the Earth being suddenly heated by the Sun's fiercer Beams, the Roots are rather scorched and dried up in the Earth, than nourish'd; so that the Plant consisting only of watry parts, is consumed, as it were, by Fire: sometimes hopeful Plants, when by a sudden Gust some Master Veins are broken, if sudden heat ensues, they likewise Fire: for being not come to maturity, and being deprived of the Supports of Life and Vegetation, they likewise perish, are dried up, and fall to dust. *French-men* they call those Plants, whose Leaves do not spread and grow large, but rather spire upwards, and grow tall; these Plants they do not

[43] Usually planted after February 1 in Virginia today.
[44] The practice of covering seedbeds with brush of various kinds continued until replaced by the familiar cloth covering in use today in the South. This did not occur until the end of the nineteenth century.

tend, being not worthy their Labour. Were they so Critical, I believe, they might have great Guess what Plants were most likely to turn *French-men,* by observing whether the Roots of the Plants run downwards; as those whose Branches are aptest to spire upwards: for tho' I have not made positive proof thereof, I have something more than bare fancy for my conjecture; I have pull'd up some of these *French-men,* and compar'd them with the Roots of some other Plants, and I found them much longer than others;[45] and 'tis observable, loose Soyls, and sandy Ground, are more subject thereto than the stiff Land. The Country of itself is one entire Wood, consisting of large Timber Trees of several sorts, free from Thickets or under Wood, the small Shrubs growing only on Lands, that have been cleared, or in Swamps; and thus it is for several Hundreds of Miles, even as far as has yet been discover'd. But that shall be reserv'd 'till another opportunity.

I am, etc.

[45] This statement is in contrast to that of Wolf, who pictures a plant showing the "usual type of frenching, leaves numerous, thick, erect, and narrow. Root system poorly developed" (*Tobacco Diseases,* p. 38) .

VII

"A COMMISSION . . . FOR . . . THE DISCOVERY OF THE SOUTH SEA"

Copy of a Journal from Virginia beyond the Apalachin mountains in Sept. 1671 by Mr. Clayton & read Aug. 1, 1688, before the Society.[1]

Thomas Batts   Thomas Woods, & Robert Fallam[2] Haveing received a Commission from the honorable Major General

[1] Taken from the manuscript in the B. M., Sloane MSS 4432, f. 9. Clayton copied Robert Fallam's account of the journey. The copy of the journal appearing in the Journal Book of the Royal Society (No. 8, p. 223) abbreviates many words which were given in full in Mr. Clayton's original letter. Some differing versions of Clayton's copy of the journal have been previously printed: Berthold Fernow, *Ohio Valley in Colonial Days* (Albany, 1890), pp. 220–29; *William and Mary Quarterly,* ser. 1, XV (1907), 234–41; D. I. Bushnell, Jr., "Virginia – From Early Records," *American Anthropologist,* IX (1907), 45–56; Alvord and Bidgood, *First Explorations,* pp. 183–95. All these versions have a few omissions and differ slightly in spelling and punctuation from the one given here. In addition to Clayton, Dr. Daniel Coxe made a copy of the journal which he sent to England in March 1687. This is now in the Public Record Office, Colonial Papers, xxvii, No. 42, and was published in *New York Colonial Documents* (Albany, 1853–87), III, 193–97. Dr. Coxe's copy is written in the third person and differs somewhat from Clayton's in other ways. Dr. John Mitchell, about seventy years later, traced the route followed by the expedition in a paper for the Royal Society, "Remarks on the Journal of Batts and Fallam; in their Discovery of the Western Parts of Virginia in 1671" (B. M., Sloane MSS 4432, f. 3).

[2] Thomas Batts, grandson of Robert Batts, "fellow and vicar-master of University College, Oxford," had been in Virginia at least fourteen years. His will is on record at Henrico County courthouse, according to Alvord and Bidgood, *First Explorations,* p. 184). In the *William and Mary Quarterly,* ser. 1, XV (1907), 234–41, Thomas Woods is identified as a son of General Wood, but no reference is given. Robert Fallam is unidentified.

Wood[3] for the finding out of the ebbing & flowing of the Water on the other Side of the Mountains in order to the discovery of the South Sea, accompanied with Perecute, a great man of the Apomatack Indians, & Jack Neasan, formerly Servant to Major General Wood,[4] with five horses set forward from Apomatacks town[5] about eight of the Clock in the morning, being Friday Sept 1st, 1671. That day we traveled about 40 miles took up our quarters & found that we had traveled from the Okonocker path due West.[6]

Sept. 2   We traveled about 45 miles & came to our quarters at Sun set, & found we were to the North of the West.

Sept. 3   We traveled West & by South Courses, & about three o'Clock came to a great Swamp a mile & a half or two miles over, & very difficult to pass. We led our horses thro', & waded twice over a Run emptying itself into Roanoke River. After we were over, we went north west, & so came round & took up our quarters Nigh West. This day we travelled 40 miles good.

Sept. 4.   We set forward, & about two of the Clock, arrived at the Sapony Indian Town.[7] We travelled South & by West courses till about noon, & came to the Sapony West.

[3] Abraham Wood (1610–80?). As a captain, Wood had commanded the new Fort Henry in 1645, and there he lived for over thirty years, trading with the Indians and exploring to the west.

[4] The General had been an indentured servant as a boy, too.

[5] The most important village of the Appomattoc tribe, with a population about 250. It was situated across the river from Fort Henry, and General Wood employed many of these Indians as guides.

[6] They started out on the famous Occaneechee trail, leading to an Indian town on the border of North Carolina and thence to Augusta, Georgia. Later, they turned onto a less-traveled Indian trail to the west.

[7] The Saponis were one of the Sioux tribes and had several villages in Campbell County. The largest one, numbering approximately 1,000, was on a tributary of the Staunton River, near the present town of Altavista. It had been visited by John Lederer the previous year. Here the Otter and Staunton rivers fork, and the explorers followed the latter.

Here we were very joyfully & kindly received with firing of guns & plenty of provisions. We here hired a Sapony Indian to be our Guide towards the Totemas a nearer way than usual.

Sept. 5.   Just as we were ready to take horse, & march from the Saponys, about Seven of the Clock in the morning, we heard some guns go off from the other side of the River. They were Seven Apomatack Indians sent by Major General Wood to accompany us in our Voyage. We hence sent back a horse belonging to Mr. Thomas Wood, which was tired, by a Portugal belonging to Major General Wood, whom we here found. About eleven of the Clock we set forward & that night came to the Town of the Hanahaskins[8] which we judge to be 25 miles from the Saponys & received the like or better entertainment than from the Saponys. The town lying West & by North is an Island on the Sapony River with Lands.

Sept. 6.   About 11 of the Clock we set forward from the Hanahaskins but left Mr. Thomas Wood at the Town dangerously sick of the Flux, & the horse he rode on belonging to Major General Wood was likewise taken with the Staggers, & a failing in his hinder parts.[9] Our Course was this day West by South, & we took up our quarters West about 20 miles from town. This afternoon our horses stray'd away about ten of the Clock.

Sept. 7.   We set forward about three of the Clock. We had sight of the Mountains. We travelled 25 Miles over very hilly & stony Ground; and our Course Westerly.

Sept. 8.   We set out by Sunrise & traveled all day a West & by north course. About one of the Clock we came to a Tree

[8] Monahassanugh (?), one of the Sioux tribes. Their main town, with a population of roughly 1,000, was a mile and a half up the James River from Wingina, in Nelson County.

[9] An equine disease which causes a loss of equilibrium, often known as "blind staggers."

marked in the path with a coal ⋀⋀Λ ΝŦ .[10] About four of
the Clock we came to the foot of the first Mountain, went to
the top, & then came to a small Descent, & so did rise again; &
then till we came almost to the bottom was a very steep
Descent. We travelled all day over very stony Rocky ground,
& after 30 miles travell this day we came to our quarters at the
foot of the Mountain due West. We past the Sapony River
twice this day.

Sept. 9. We were stiring with the Sun, & traveled West,
& after a little riding came again to the Sapony River, where it
was very narrow, & ascended the second Mountain, which
wound up West & by South with several risings & fallings, after
which we came to a steep descent, at the foot whereof was a
lovely descending Valley[11] about 6 miles over, with curious
small risings; indifferent good way. Our course over it was
South West. After we were over that, we came to a very steep
descent, at the foot whereof stood the Totema Town in a very
rich swamp between a branch & the main River of Roanoke,
circled about with Mountains.[12] We got hither about three of
the Clock, after we had traveled 25 miles. Here we were
exceedingly civilly entertained. Saturday night, Sunday, &
Monday we staid at the Totema, Perecute being taken very
sick of a fever & ague every afternoon. Not withstanding on
Tuesday morning about nine of the Clock we resolved to leave
our horses with the Totemas & set forward.

Sept. 12. We left the town West & by North. We
travelled that day sometimes southerly sometimes northerly, as

[10] Dr. John Mitchell believed that these were the inverted initials of Abraham Wood and James Needham, but Alvord and Bidgood dismiss such an as-
sumption "as interesting, but hardly correct" (*First Explorations*, p. 201, n.).
Nevertheless, there is no proof that Needham had not done some exploring
for Wood before he came to South Carolina in September of 1670. His
later expeditions for Wood are well known.

[11] They had crossed over the Blue Ridge into the Roanoke Valley.

[12] Roanoke.

the path went over Several high mountains & steep Vallies
crossing several branches & the River Roanoke several times,
all exceedingly stony ground, until about four of the Clock
Perecute being taken with his fit & we very weary we took up
our quarters by the side of Roanoke River almost at the
head of it at the foot of the great Mountain.[13]   Our course was
west & north, having travelled 25 miles.   At the Totemas we
hired one of their Indians for our Guide, left one of the
Apomatack Indians there sick.

Sept. 13.   In the morning we set forward early.   After we
had travelled about three miles we came to the foot of the
Great Mountain; & found a very steep ascent, so that we could
never keep ourselves from sliding down again.   It continued
for three miles with small Intermissions of better way.   Right
up by the path on the left we saw the proportion of the man
<whereof they had given an account, it seems, in a former
Relation, which I have not> there growing very high, weeds &
grasses about it; but nothing but Maze on the place.[14]   When
we were got up to the top of the Mountain & set down very
weary we saw very high mountains lying to the north & south
as far as we could discover.   Our course up the Mountain was
west by north, a very small descent on the other side, & as soon
as ever we found the Vallies tending westerly.   It was a
pleasing tho' dreadfull sight to see mountains & Hills as if
piled one upon another.[15]   After we had travelled about three
miles from the Mountains easily descending ground, about 12
of the Clock we came to two trees mark'd with Coal

/X\\ /V干 , the other cut with /X\ /\ 干 & several other

[13] Almost at the source of the Roanoke (Staunton) River.
[14] Clayton added the phrases in brackets.   The old Virginian Railway ap-
proximated the old trail traveled by the expedition from the present site of
Roanoke to the New River.
[15] This point marks the limit of the eastern watershed.

scrabblements.[16]   Hard by a Runn just like the Swift Creek at
Mr Randolph's in Virginia,[17] emptying itself sometimes westerly, sometimes northerly, with curious meadows on each
side.   Going forward we found rich ground, but stony, curious
rising hills, & brave Meadows with grass above man's height,
many Rivers running west north west, & several runs from the
Southerly Mountains, which we saw as we march'd, which run
northerly into the great River.   After we had travelled about 7
miles, we came to a very steep descent, where we found a great
run, which emptied itself as we suppose, into the great River
northerly, our course being as the path went west southwest.[18]
We set forward west & had not gone far, but we met again with
the River still broad, running West & by North.   We went
over the great run emptying itself northerly into the great
River.   After we had marched about 6 miles northwest & by
north, we came to the River again, where it was much broader
than at the two other places.   It ran here west & by south, & so,
as we suppose, wound up westerly.   Here we took up our
quarters, after we had wad'd over, for this night.   Due west,
the soil the further we went, the richer, stony, full of brave
meadows & old fields <old fields is a common Expression for
land, that has been cultivated by Indians, & left fallow which
are generally overrun with what they call Broome grasses.>
    Sept. 14th.   We set forward before Sunrise, our provi-

[16] Again the expedition had been preceded by the unknown explorers who
had first seen the eastern continental divide.

[17] Henry Randolph, uncle of William Randolph (1651–1711), lived at
Turkey Island on the northern bank of the James River, about 40 miles
above Jamestown.   There the peninsulas of bottom land formed rich
meadows.   Since Swift Creek is not capitalized in the Alvord and Bidgood
version, it is identified specifically as "Swift Creek" (in a footnote on p. 188)
which empties into the Appomattox near Petersburg and which was called
"Randolph's River" in 1670.

[18] This was New River, then called Wood's River.   The party first crossed
it not far from the present town of Radford.

sion being all spent.   We travelled as the path went, sometimes southerly, sometimes northerly, over good ground, but stony, sometimes rising Hills, & then steep Descents.   As we marched in a clear place at the top of a hill we saw agst us lying southwest a curious prospect of hills like waves rais'd by a gentle breeze of Wind rising one after another.   Mr Batts supposed he saw houses;[19] but I rather think them to be white cliffs.   We marched about 20 miles this day, & about three of the Clock took up our quarters to see, if our Indians could kill us some Deer, being west & by north very weary & hungry; & Perecute continued very ill, yet desirous to go forward.   We came this Day over several brave runs & hope tomorrow to see the main River again.

Sept. 15.   Yesterday in the afternoon & this Day we lived a Dog's life, hungry & Dased.   Our Indians having done their best could kill us no meat.   The Deer, they said were in such herds, & the ground so dry, that one or other of them would spy them.   No remedy.   About one of the clock we set forward, & went about 15 miles over some exceeding good some indifferent ground, a West & by north course till we came to a great run, that empties itself west & by north as we suppose, into the Great River, which we hope is nigh at hand.   As we marched, we met with some wild gooseberrys & exceeding large haws, with which we were forced to feed ourselves.

Sept. 16.   Our guide went from us yesterday, & we saw him no more till we return'd to the Totemas.   Our Indians went aranging betimes to see & kill us some Deer or Meat. One came & told us they heard a Drum & a Gun go off to the northward.   They brought us some exceeding good Grapes, &

---

[19] Alvord and Bidgood have used "sayles" rather than "houses"; however, the manuscripts at the British Museum and the Royal Society of London both say "houses," as does Coxe's version.

killed two turkies, which were very welcome, & with which we feasted ourselves, & about ten of the Clock set forward, & after we had traveled about 10 miles one of our Indians killed us a Deer, & presently afterwards we had sight of a curious River like Apomatack River: Its course here was north, & so, as we suppose runs west about certain curious mountains we saw westward. Here we took up our quarters, our course having been west. We understand the Mohecan Indians did here formerly live. It cannot be long since, for we found Corn stalks in the ground.[20]

Sept. 17. Early in the morning we went to seek some trees to mark and the Indians being impatient of longer stay, by reason it was like to be bad Weather, & that it was so difficult to get provision.[21] We found four trees exceeding fit for our purpose, that had been half barked by our Indians standing after one the other. We first proclaimed the King in these Words "Long live Charles the Second, by the grace of God King of England, Scotland, France & Ireland, & Virginia, & of all the Territories thereunto belonging, Defender of the Faith etc;" fired some Guns & went to the first tree, which we

marked thus with a pair of marking Irons for his sacred Majesty; then the

next thus $\mathcal{W}\beta$ for the right honorable Governor Sr. William

---

[20] Dr. Ben C. McCary says that little is known of the "Mohetan" tribe, a member of the Sioux, and that there is only one source concerning them. They inhabited the mountains on the upper part of the New River (*Indians in Seventeenth-Century Virginia* [Williamsburg, Va., 1957], p. 10). Alvord and Bidgood called them "Cherokees."

[21] Peter's Falls, the farthest point reached by this expedition, is where the New River passes through Peter's Mountain in Giles County, Va., an area drained by the Ohio, on the border of present-day West Virginia.

Berkeley; the third thus $\mathcal{AW}$ for the honble Major General
Wood; the last thus $\mathcal{B}:\mathcal{RF}.\mathcal{P}.$ for Perecute, who said he
would be an Englishman; & on another Tree hard by stands
these Letters one under another $\mathcal{EN}.TT.NP:V.ER.$ [22]
After we had done, we went ourselves down to the River's
side, but not without great difficulty, it being a piece of very
rich ground, whereon the Mohecans had formerly lived, &
grown up so with Weeds & small prickly Locusts & Thistles to
a very great height, that it was almost impossible to pass. It
cost us hard labour to get thro'. When we came to the River
side, we found it better & broader than expected, much like
James River at Col: Stagg's, the falls much like those falls. [23]
We imagined by the Water marks, that it flows here about three
feet. It was ebbing Water, when we were here. We set up a
stick by the Water side, but found it ebb very Slowly. Our
Indians kept such a hallowing, that we durst not stay any longer
to make further tryall. Immediately upon coming to our
Quarters, we returned homewards, and when we were on the
top of a Hill, we turned about, & saw over against us westerly
over a certain delightful hill a fog arise, & a glimmering light as
from Water. We suppose there to be a great Bay. We came to
the Totemas Tuesday night, where we found our horses well,
& ourselves well entertain'd. We immediately had the news of
Mr Byrd & his great company's Discovery three miles from the
Totemas town. [24] We here found a Mohecan Indian, who having intelligence of our coming were afraid it had been to fight
them, & had sent him to the Totemas to enquire. We gave

[22] No theories have been advanced as to the owners of these initials.
[23] Thomas Stegg, uncle of William Byrd I, built a house at the falls of the
James River in 1661.
[24] As a wilderness merchant, Byrd was Wood's principal competitor and at
the latter's death Byrd emerged as the prime Indian trader.

him satisfaction to the contrary, & that we came as friends, presented him with three or four shots of powder. He told us by our Interpreter, that we had been from the Mountains half way to the place they now lived at: That the next Town beyond them lived upon plain level, from whence came abundance of Salt: That he could inform us no further by reason that there were a very great company of Indians, that lived upon the Great Water.[25]

Sept. 24.   After very civil Entertainment we came from the Totemas, & on Sunday morning the 24th we came to the Hanahaskins. We found Mr. Wood dead & buried, & his horse likewise dead. After civil entertainment with firing of Gunns at parting, which is more than usual.

Sept. 25.   On Monday morning we came from thence, and reached to the Saponys that night, where we stayed till Wednesday.

Sept. 27.   We came from thence, they having been very courteous to us. At night we came to the Apomatak Town, being very wet & weary.

Oct. 1.   Being Sunday morning we arrived safe at Fort Henry. God's holy name be praised for our preservation.

[25] Lake Erie. James Mooney located the area containing a salt source as possibly near the Mercer Salt Works on New River, West Virginia, or else at Salt Pond in Giles County ("Siouan Tribes of the East," *Bulletin of the Bureau of Ethnology*, XXII [Washington, 1894] p. 36).

VIII

"BUT TIS STRANGE
IN HOW MANY THINGS . . . THEY ARE REMISE,
WCH ONE WOULD THINK ENGLISH MEN
SHOULD NOT BE GUILTY OF"[1]

Sir

My last was the journal of Thomas Bats, Thomas Woods, &
Rob't Fallam. I know Coll. Byrd very well, that's mentioned
to have been about that time as far as the Totemas. He's one
of the intelligentest Gentlemen in all Virginia, & Knows more
of Indian affairs than any man in the Country. I discoursed
him about the River on the other side of the mountains, said to
ebb & flow which he assured me was a mistake in them, for that
it must run into a Lake now caled Lake Petite, which is fresh
Water, for since that time a Colony of the French are comne
down from Canada, & have seated themselves on the back of
Virginia, where Fallam, & the rest supposed there might be a
Bay, but is a Lake, to wch they have given the name of Lake
Petite, there being Several Larger Lakes twixt that & Canada.
The French possessing themselves of these Lakes, no doubt
will in short time be absolute Masters of the Beaver Trade, the

---

[1] Taken from the manuscript in the Archives of the Royal Society of London,
Classified Papers C 2.21/1–7 (see Plate II, facing p. 33). The letter was also
printed in *Phil. Trans.*, XVII (1693), 978–88. The printed version differs
very little from the original, except for the first paragraph and the omission of
the small sketch of Jamestown. The letter was written by Clayton from
Wakefield, August 17, 1688, and read October 24, according to notes on an
extract from his letter in the Supplement to the Letter Books of the Royal
Society, Vol. II, f. 483.

greatest number of Beavers being catchd there.[2]   The Coll:
told me likewise that the common Notion of the Lake of
Canada, he was assured was a mistake, for the River supposed
to come out of it had no Communication wth any of the Lakes,
nor the Lakes one wth another, but were distinct.   But not to
ramble after hear say, & other matters.   But with them[?] to
return to the parts of Virginia inhabited by the English, wch in
general is a very firtile Soile far surpassing England, for there
English Wheat <as they call it to distinguish it from Maze
commonly caled Virginia Wheat> yields generaly twixt 15 &
thirty fold, the ground only once plowd, where as tis a good
crop in England that yields above 8 fold, after all their toile &
labour.[3]   And yet in truth 'tis only the barrenest parts that
they have cultivated, – tilling and planting only the high
Lands, leaveing the Ritcher vales unstird, because they understand not any thing of draining.   So that the ritchest meadow
lands, wch is one third of the Country, is boggy marsh, &
swamp, where of they make little advantage, but loose in them
abundance of their Cattle, espetialy at the first of the Spring,
when the Cattle are weake, & venture too far, after young
grasse.   Where as vast improvemts might be made thereof, for
the generality of Virginia is a sandy Land wth a shallow soile.
So that after they have cleard a fresh piece of ground out of the
woods, it will not beare Tobacco past two or three years,

[2] At this time England was very much concerned with the extension of the
French empire.   In 1671 the French had made formal claim to all the Great
Lakes, and two years later Marquette and Joliet had explored the Mississippi.
They were followed by La Salle, who unsuccessfully attempted to take pos-
session of the mouth of that great river in 1684.

[3] M. Durand, who arrived in Virginia in 1686, a few months after Clayton
had departed, remarked upon the great fertility of the soil, adding that some
of the land was much richer than other parts.   The topsoil in Gloucester
County, he said, reached a depth of six inches (Durand de Dauphiné,
A Huguenot Exile in Virginia, ed. Gilbert Chinard [New York, 1934], p. 114) .

unlesse Cow pend, for they manure their ground by keeping
their Cattle, as in the South you doe your sheep, ev'ry night
confineing them within hurdles, wch they remove when they
have sufficiently dungd one Spot of ground, but alas they
cannot improve mch thus, besides it produces a strong sort of
Tobacco in wch the Smoakers say they can plainly taste the
fullsomness of the dungg. Therefore ev'ry three or four years
they must be for clearing a new piece of ground out of woods,
wch requires mch Labour & toile, it being so thick grown all
over with massy timber.[4] Thus their Plantations run over vast
Tracts of ground, each ambitioning to engrosse as mch as they
can, that they may be sure [to] have enough to plant, & for
their Stocks and herds of Cattle to range & feed in, that
Plantations of 1000, 2000, or 3000 Acres are Common,
whereby the Country is thinly inhabited, their liveing is solitary & unsociable;[5] tradeing confused, & dispersed; besides
other inconveniencys, whereas they might improve 200 or 300
Acres to more advantage, & would make the Country mch
more healthy, for those that have 3000 Acres have scarse cleard
600 Acres thereof, wch is peculiarly termd the plantation,
being surrounded wth the 2400 Acres of Woods. So that there
can be no free or even motion of the Aire. But the Aire is kept
either stagnant, or the lofty sulphurious particles of the aire,
that are higher than the tops of the trees, wch are above as high

[4] Garner said this was the general seventeenth-century practice in the Tidewater where the soil was very sandy and that tobacco produced on "dunged"
land was not only strong but burned very poorly (*Production of Tobacco,*
p. 24). Even as late as 1793 Jefferson wrote to Washington that "we can buy
an acre of new land cheaper than we can manure an old acre" (*Thomas
Jefferson's Garden Book,* ed. E. M. Betts [Philadelphia, 1944], p. 191).
[5] Brooks placed the average size of the seventeenth-century plantation at
5,000 acres, with some even as large as 37,000 (*The Mighty Leaf,* p. 98).
Wertenbaker disagrees strongly with this view. He cites Bruce as having
"worked out the averages from thousands of patents" and found them to be
674 acres for the period 1651–1700 (T. J. Wertenbaker, *The First Americans,
1607–1690* [New York, 1927], II, 29).

again as the generality of the woods in England, descending
when they pass over the cleard spots of ground, must needs in
the violent heat of Summer, raise a preternatural fermt, &
produce bad effects.   Nor is it any advantage to their Stocks, or
Crops, for did they but drain their swamps, & Low Lands, they
have a very deep Soile that would endure planting, 20, or 30
years, & some would scarse ever be worn out, but be ever
longer better, for they might lay them all winter, or when they
pleasd in water, & the product of their labour would be double
or treble, whether corn or Tobacco; & that this is no fond
projection, <tho when I discoursed the same to several, & in
part shown them how their particular grounds might be
draind at a very easy rate> they have either been so conceited
of their old way, so sottish as not to apprehend; or so negligent
as not to apply themselves thereto.[6]   But on the Plantation
where I lived, I draind a good large Swamp, wch fully answered expectation.   The Gentlewoman where I lived, was a
very acute ingenious Lady Who one day discourseing the
overseer of her Servants, about pitching the ensuing years
Crop.   The overseer was nameing one place where he designd
to plant 30,000 plants, another place for 15000 another for
10,000 & so forth the whole Crop designd to be about 100,000
plants Haveing observd the year before, he had done the like,
& scatterd his Crop up & down the plantation, at places a mile
or a mile & a halfe asunder, wch was very inconvenient, &
whereby they lost mch time.   I interposed & askd why they did
not plant all their Crop together.   The fellow smiled as it were
at my ignorance, & said, there was very good reason for it, I
replyd, that was it I enquired, after.   He returnd the Plantation had been an old, Planted Plantation, & being but a smal
plot of ground was almost worn out, so that they had not

[6] Clayton might have viewed with more approval than do present-day scientists the current destruction of the Dismal Swamp.

ground all together that would bring forth Tobacco. I told him then they had better ground than ever yet they had planted, & more than their hands could manage. He smiled again, & asked me where, I then named such a swamp. He then said scornfully he thought wt a planter I was, that I understood better how to make a Sermon than manageing Tobacco, I replyd wth some warmness tho I hoped so, that was impertinence, & no answer. He then sd, that the Tobacco there would drown, & the Rootes Rott, I replyd that the whole Country would drown if the Rivers were stopd, but it might be laid as drye as any land on the plantation. In short we discoursed it very warmly, till he told me he understood his own business well enough, & did not desire to learn of me. But the Gentlewoman attended somewt better to my reasoning, & got me one day to goe, & show her how I projected the draining of the Swamp, & thought it so feasible, that she was resolvd to have it done, & therefore desired me I would again, – discourse her Overseer, wch I did several times, but he would by no means harken thereto, & was so positive, that she was forced to turn him away to have her Servts set about the work; & wth three men in thirteen days I draind the whole Swamp, it being Sandy land soaks, & drains admirably well, & wt I little expected, laid a Well drie at a considerable distance, the Gentlewoman was in England last Yeare, & I think Dr. Moulin was by when she asked me. Now to teach her, how she might make her Tobacco that grew in that Swamp less, for it produced so very large, that it was suspected to be of the Aranoko kind, I told her, tho the complaint was rare, yet there was an excellent remedy for that, in leting evry plant beare 8 or 9 leaves instead of four or five, & she would have more Tobacco, & less Leaves.[7] Now you must know they Top their

---

[7] The world-wide market being saturated by tobacco, the first crop control seems to have been instituted in 1621, when Sir Francis Wyatt's government directed that each plant be limited to nine leaves (Brooks, *The Mighty Leaf*,

Tobacco, that is take away the little top budd, when the Plant has put forth as many leaves as they think the Ritchness of the ground will bring to a Substance, but generaly when it has shot forth four or six leaves. And when the Top budd is gone, it puts forth no more Leaves, but side branches, wch they call Suckers, wch they are carefull ever to take away, that they may not impoverish the Leaves,[8] I have been more tedious in the particulars, the fullyer to evince, how resolute they are, & conceitedly bent to follow their old practice, & custom, rather than to receive directions from others, tho plain, easy, and advantageous; there are many other places are as easy to drain as this, tho' of larger extent, and ritcher Soile, for some of wch I have given directions, & have only had the return perhaps of a flout afterwards: Even in James Town Island wch is mch wt of an Oval figure, there's a Swamp runs Diagonal wise over the Island whereby is lost at least 150 Acres of Land that would be meadow wch would turn to as good account as if it were in England. Besides it is the great anoyance of the Town and no doubt but makes it mch more unhealthy. If therefore they but scourd the Channel, and made a pretty ordinary Trench all along the middle of the Swamp, placed a Sluce at the mouth where it opens into the Back Creek for the mouth of the Channel there is narrow has a good hard bottom, & is not past two yards deep when the flood is out, as if nature had designd it beforehand, they might thus drain all the Swamp absolutely dry, or lay it under water at their pleasure. I have talkd several times here of to Mr. Sherwood,[9] the Owner of the

---

p. 96). Garner said that the 1628 act set the number of leaves at twelve per plant, in contrast to the usual 25–30 leaves (*Production of Tobacco,* p. 25).

[8] The Virginians adopted from the Indians this practice of removing the terminal bud to encourage leaf growth. Robert said that some farmers did their own topping by using their thumbnail, which had been grown long for the purpose and hardened in a flame (*Story of Tobacco,* p. 18).

[9] William Sherwood, at that time a member of the House of Burgesses, representing James City County. See pp. xxx–xxxi.

Swamp, yet nothing is essayd in order thereto.   And now since
we are speaking of James Town, give me leave to adjoyne some
reflections as to the Situation, & fortifications of the place.
The natural Situation of the place is such, as perhaps the world
has not a more commodious place for a Town, where all things
conspire for advantage thereof, to give you some Idea of the
place the River & Island lie thus.[10] [For the map of Jamestown,
see the facing page.]

  James Town Island is rather a Peninsula, being joynd to the
Continent, by a smal neck of Land, not past 20 or 30 yards
over, & wch at Spring Tides is overflowd, and is then an
absolute Island.   now they have built a silly sort of a fort, that
is a brick Wall in the shape of a halfe moone, at the Begining of
the Swamp, because the Channel of the River lies very nigh
the Shoare, but it is the same as if a fort were built at Chelsey to
secure London from being taken by Shiping.   Besides Ships
passing up the River are secured from the Guns of the fort, till
they come directly over against the fort by reason the fort
stands in a vale, & all the Guns directed down the River, that
should play on the Ships, as they are coming up the River, will
Lodge their Shot wthin ten twenty or forty yards in the rising
bank, wch is mch above the Level of the fort, So that if a Ship
gave but a good broad side, just when she comes to beare upon
the fort, She might put the fort into that confusion, as to have
free passage enough.   There was indeed an old fort of earth
in the Town, being a sort of Tetragone, wth somthing like
Bastions at the four Corners, as I remember, but the Chanel
lyeing further off to the middle of the River there, they let it
be demolished, & built that new one spoake of, of Brick wch
seemes little better than a blind Wall, to shoot wild Ducks or

[10] For more details, see C. A. Browne, "Reverend Dr. John Clayton and His
Early Map of Jamestown, Virginia," *William and Mary Quarterly*, ser. 2,
XIX (1939), 1–7.

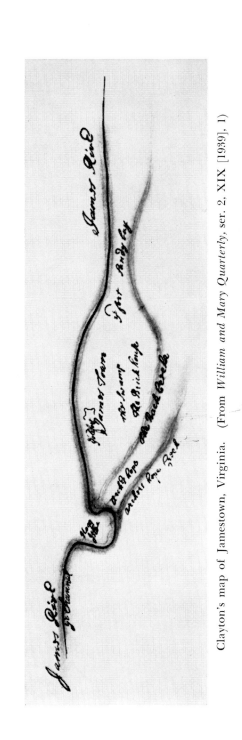

Clayton's map of Jamestown, Virginia.   (From *William and Mary Quarterly*, ser. 2, XIX [1939], 1)

Geese.[11] If they would build a Fort for the Security of the Town & Country, I conceive it should be on Archers hope point,[12] for that would stop the Ships from passing up the River, before they came to the Town, & would secure the Town from being blockd up by Sea. The Channel at Archer's Hope point, lies close by the Shoare, & makes such an Angle there by Reason of Hogg Island,[13] that goeing up or down the River, let the Wind be where it will, they must there bring the Contrary Tack on board, and generally when they About the Ship as they call it, they are so nigh the shoare, that a man may almost fling a finger stone on board. How mch this hinders the motion of a Ship, & wt confusion it must be, to them to bring a contrary Tack on board, whilst they have all the Guns of a fort playing so nigh upon them, may readily be conceivd, Archers Hope is a neck of Land, that runs down three miles long, not mch past halfe a mile broad betwixt the main River & Archers Hope Creek, wch has large Marshes & Swamps. So that a Citadel built upon the point, would almost be impregnable, being it could be attackd no way but one, wch is so narrow a slender neck of Land, that it would be difficult to take it that way. And it would secure James Town from being blockd being it would not be past a mile by Water, to the point

[11] Durand wrote, "I crossed the York river opposite a brick fort, where there are 20 or 25 fine guns" (*A Huguenot Exile*, p. 136). S. H. Yonge, however, was inclined to agree with Clayton on the impracticability of the fort ("The Site of Old 'James Towne' 1607–1698," *Va. Mag. Hist. Biog.*, XII [1904], 127). The fort was one of the five constructed under an act of the Assembly passed in September of 1667. The contractors were Matthew Page, Theophilus Hone, and Colonel William Drummond. The money not being available until 1672, they were not completed until 1676. The "tetragone," or square fort, was probably that known to have been built on land patented in 1624 by Captain Ralph Hamor. Its date of construction and location are unknown today.

[12] Named for Gabriel Archer, an early member of the Virginia Council.

[13] Among the improvements made by Captain John Smith in the winter of 1608/9 was the removal of the pigs from Jamestown proper to Hog Island, located a few miles below the town.

of James Town Island.   The Island is so surrounded wth
water, & marshie land, that the Town could never be Bombd
by land.   But now to return to the Reflections of Improveing,
and manureing of Land in Virginia, hitherto, as I have said,
they have used none but that of Cowpening,   Yet I suppose
they might find very good marle[14] in many places   I have seen
both the Red and Blew marle at some breakes of Hills,   This
would be the properest manure for their Sandy land, if they
spread it not too thick, theirs being, as I have sd a shallow,
sandy Soile, wch was the Reason I never advised any to use
Lime, tho they have very good Lime of Oyster shells, but thats
the properest manure for cold Clay land, & not for a Sandy
Soile.   But as most Lands have one Swamp or another border-
ing on them, they may certainly get admirable Slitch,[15] wherewth to manure all their uplands.   But this say they, will not
improve ground, but clods & grows hard, tis true, it will doe so
for some time, a year or two at the first, but did they cast it in
heaps, & let it lye for two or three years after a frost or two had
seizd it, & it had been well pierced therewth, I doubt not it
would turn to good account, & for this too I have some thing
more than bare conjecture, for discourseing it once wth a good
notable Planter, we went to view a heap thereof, that casualy
he had cast up twixt three and four years before, & we found it
not very binding, but rather a fine natural mold, whereupon
he did confess, he then remembered that out of a ridge of the
like mold he had had very large Plants, wch must have been of
the like slime or slitch cast up before.   But sd, that himselfe &
others despaird of this manure, because they had taken of this
slitch fresh & moist out of the Swamp, and filld Tobacco hills

[14] Marl is a deposit, composed mainly of clay mixed with calcium carbonate.
It is used on soils deficient in lime.
[15] Soil dredged from the swamps.

wth it, and in the midst of it planted their plants, wch so bound
the Rootes, of their plants,[16] that they never came to any thing.
but he sd, he then saw his error, yet I have not heard he has
rememberd to correct it.   But tis strange in how many things
besides they are remise, wch one would think English men
should not be guilty of.[17]   They neither house nor milk any of
their Cows in Winter, haveing a Notion that it would kill
them[18] yet I perswaded the aforementioned Lady where I
lived, to milk four Cows the last Winter that I staid in the
Country, whereof she found so good effect, that she assured me
she would keep to my advice for the future, & also as I had
further urged house them too, for wch they have mighty
conveniencys, their Tobacco houses being empty ever at that
time of the yeare, & may easily be fitted in two or three days
time wthout any prejudice, whereby their cattle would be mch
shelterd from those pinching sharp frosts that some nights on a
suddain become very severe.   I had another project for the
preservation of their Cattle proved very successfull, I urged
the Lady to sow her wheat as early as possibly she could, so that
before winter it might be well rooted, to be early & flourishing
at the first of the Spring.   So that she might turn thereon her
weake cattle, & such as should at any time be swampd, whereby
they might be recruited and Saved, & it would doe the wheat
good also.   I advised her likewise to save, & carefully gather her
Indian corn tops, & blades, & all her straw, & wt ever could be
made fodder, for her Cattle, for they get no hay, tho I was

[16] The tobacco plant is very dependent upon oxygen–carbon dioxide exchange through aeration of its roots.

[17] Zirkle defends the agricultural practices of the colonists.   He contends that they were doing all they could in the absence of knowledge of mineral fertilizers (Conway Zirkle, "John Clayton and Our Colonial Botany," *Va. Mag. Hist. Biog.*, LXVII [1959], 284–94).   Clayton would certainly not agree!

[18] Durand also remarked on the lack of barns and stables (*A Huguenot Exile*, p. 120).   This poor husbandry is practiced today in certain parts of Virginia.

urgeing her to that too, & to sow Sainfoin,[19] for being a Sandy
Soile I'me confident, it would turn to very good account;
They have little or no grasses in Winter, so that their cattle are
pin'd & starved, and many that are brought low & weake, when
the Spring begins, venture too far into the Swamps after the
fresh grasse, where they perish, so that several persons lose 10,
20, or 30 head of Cattle in a yeare, I obervd this was mch
owing to their inadvertency & error in their way of manageing
& feeding them; for they get little fodder, but as they think
Corn being more nourishing, feed them wth their Indian
Corn, wch they give them morning & evening, they spend thus
a great quantity of corn, & when all's done wt signifies two or
three heads of corn to a beast in a morning, it makes them only
linger about the houses for more, & after that sweet food they
are not so prompt to brouse on the trees, & the course grasse
wch the Country affords. So that thus their guts shrink up,
they become Belly Shot as they call it. I advised therefore
never to give them any thing in a morning, whereby as soon as
they were set forth of the Cow penns they would fall a feeding,
and tho they filld their bellys only wth such course stuff as had
little nourishmt in it, yet it would keep out their bellys, & they
would have a better digestion, & then when they were comne
home at nights, to fodder them, beginning wth Straw & their
coursest fodder, wch they would learn to eat by degrees, before
they tasted that that was more delicate, & whilst their digestion
was strong, would yield them nourishmt to keep them still so,
afterwards when the winter pinchd, their fine fodder then
would stand them instead, & hereby they might preserve their
weakest cattle, by these methods, & the help of the Wheat

---

[19] Sainfoin is *Onobrychis viciaefolia* Scop., a perennial forage herb of the
legume family. Jefferson was much impressed with it in France and planted
it at Monticello (*Garden Book,* p. 118) .

patch.[20] She the Gentlewoman where I lived, saved all her
Cattle, & lost not one in two winters after, that I staid there;
besides she saved above 20 barrels of Corn, as I remember that
she told me she used to spend upon her stock. And a barrel of
corn is commonly worth 10 shillings. Nay further, the last
Spring she fed two beasts, a Bullock & a Cow, fat, upon her
wheat wth the addition only of a little boild corn, & yet the
Wheat was scarse eat down enough. But to return again to the
nature of the earth, wch may be pretty well gatherd from wt I
have already said. I have observd that at 5 or 6 yards deep, at
the breakes of some banks, I have found veins of Clay, admirable good to make Potts, pipes, or the like of, & whereof I
suppose the Indians make their pipes, & potts, to boile their
meat in, wch they make very handsomly, & will endure the fire
better than most crucibles,[21] I tooke of this Clay, dryed,
poudered, & sifted it; poudered & sifted pot sheards, & glass; 3
parts, 2 parts & one part as I remember, & therewth made a
large crucible, wch was the best I yet tried in my life, I tooke it
once red hot out of the fire & clapt it imediatly into water, & it
started not at all. The Country abounds mightily wth Iron
Oare, that as I have been assured by some upon tryal, has been
found very good. There are Rocks thereof appear at the
precipice of Hills, at the foot whereof there runs a River fit for
a forge, & theres Wood enough to supply it wth Charcoal. as I
have heard there was formerly some persons undertooke the

[20] Glover confirms Clayton in saying that the colonists were careless in looking after cattle, often feeding them only the husks of corn, whereupon the
hungry cattle frequently strayed into the marshes and were lost ("An Account
of Virginia," p. 634). Cabell stated that Clayton taught his landlady "the importance of the stimulus of distension as an aid to digestion" (*Early History
of Agriculture*, p. 26).

[21] Highly polished Indian pipes of this period were made of a brown
clay, varying in shade. The coastal Indians, in making pipes or pottery, mixed
the clay with crushed oyster shells (McCary, *Indians*, pp. 25, 93).

work, & when they had made but a small quantity of Iron wch proved very good, the Indian Massacre happend, & they being higher seated than the then inhabited part of the Country, were all cut off, & the works demolishd, so that it has frightend others I think from the like attempt;[22]   besides, such a work requires a greater fund, & bank of money to carry it on, than any there are able to lay out, & for persons in England to meddle therewth, is certainly to be cheated at such a distance. Some Indians brought Coll. Byrd, some Black lead, whereof he has told me there was great Stoare.[23]   There's very curious Talk[24] towards the falls of Rapahanock River, wch they burn & make a delicate white wash of it   The Secretary of State Coll. Spencer has assured me there were vitriolick or alluminous earths[25] on the Banks of Potomack; & thus far of what my memory supplys me, refering to the Earth, in the next I shall give a short account of the Byrds.   My humble respects & service to the honble Society more peculiarly to my acquaintance & friend, I am

Sir

Yours to serve

J Clayton

Wakefield – August the 17/88

[22] This furnace lasted for three years, the massacre occurring March 22, 1622. See p. 57, n. 16.

[23] On May 26, 1686, Byrd wrote to John Clinton, ordering books on "Mineralls & Stones . . . either of mr. Boyles or any other English author" (Stanard, "Letters of William Byrd, First," p. 129) .

[24] Talc.

[25] Aluminum sulphate and other metallic sulphates.

IX

"I NEVER RECEIVED
ANY ACCOUNT . . . WHETHER THEY WERE
ACCEPTED OR REJECTED"[1]

Wakefield. Nov: 24: 1693

Richd Waller
Esq.
    Secretary to the
        Royal Society
           London

I recd yrs & pursuant thereunto have gatherd up all the scatterd Papers of those Letters wch I sent to the Honble Royal Society about Virginia. I indeed desisted giveing a further Relation thereof because I never received any account from Mr. Haley[2] to whom I sent them whether they were accepted or rejected, & indeed I was very sensible of their imperfections being I purely depended upon my memory without any minutes or notes & being full two yeares after my leaveing that Country there must be many things forgot & many errors in the Relation of those things I did remember wch I should have been more exact in had I beene upon the place, only this I can assure you there's no designed mistake but as Candid an account as I was capable of circumstances considered. Now

---

[1] Taken from the manuscript in the Archives of the Royal Society of London, Classified Papers, C 2.22. This letter to Waller precedes the article on birds 93–104, below) and was read January 3, 1693.

[2] Edmund Halley (1656–1742), astronomer and secretary of the Society at that time.

there is five years more wch takes mch of such a weake memory as mine for wch I must begg an allowance & pardon, & wthout further apologie shall obey the commands & to evince my respects be ready to expose my frailtys & weakness.   The method I think I proposed in my first letter was to give an account of the Aire & wt refers thereto then of the Waters, the Earth & Soile, the Birds the Beasts the Fishes the Plants the Insects & lastly the present state of the inhabitants but I was only come so far as the Birds wch therefore I shall give you an account of in this letter.

postscript: My Services to Mr. Houghton Esq.[8] markets for corn have altered little, they settled a little or rather stuck but now it begins to go of[f] brighter.

[8] John Houghton, agriculturist. See p. xliv. Three markets had been established in Wakefield: the weekly corn market in 1630; the cloth market in 1656; and the leather market in 1675. Wakefield was the capital of West Riding, Yorkshire (J. S. Fletcher, *A Picturesque History of Yorkshire* [London, 1900], II, 10) .

X

"THUS MUCH FOR THE BIRDS"[1]

Of the Birds

I had indeed begun once whilst I was in that Country to have made a Collection of the Birds, but falling sick of the Gripeing of the Gutts, some of them for want of care corrupted wch made them fling others away that I had thoroughly cured for I was past takeing care of them myself, there remaining but small hopes of my life.

There are 3 sorts of Eagles, the largest I take to be that they call the Gray Eagle[2] being mch the colour of our Kite or Glead.[3]

The 2d is the Bald Eagle,[4] for the body & part of the Neck being of a dark brown, the upper part of the neck & head is coverd wth a white sort of Down, whereby it looks very bald whence it is so named.

The third is the black Eagle[5] resembling most the English Eagle, they build their nests mch after the maner that Dr.

---

[1] Taken from the manuscript in the Archives of the Royal Society of London, Classified Papers, C 2.22/1–6. See p. 91, n. 1, above. The letter was printed in *Phil. Trans.*, XVII (1693), 988–99.

[2] Unidentified. W. L. McAtee has suggested "modern equivalents" for most of Clayton's birds in his "North American Bird Records in the 'Philosophical Transactions': 1665–1800," *Journal of the Society for the Bibliography of Natural History*, III, part 1 (December 1953), 46–60. Unless otherwise indicated, the Virginia bird identifications given here are taken from McAtee.

[3] A bird of prey of the falcon family, *Milvus milvus*.

[4] *Haliaeetus leucocephalus.*   [5] *Haliaeetus leucocephalus.*

Willoughby[6] describes & generaly at the top of some tall old tree naked of bows & nigh the River sides, & the people fall the Tree generaly when they take the young. They are most frequently siting on some tall tree by the River side, whence they may have a prospect up and down the River as I suppose to observe the fishing Haukes; for when they see the fishing Hauk has struck a fish immediately they take wing, & tis sometimes very pleasant to behold the flight, for when the fishing Hauk perceives herselfe pursued she will screame & make a terrible noise, till at length she lets fall the fish to make her own escape wch the Eagle frequently catches before it reach the Earth or Water. These Eagles kill young Lambs, Piggs, etc:

The Fishing Hauk[7] is an absolute species of a Kings Fisher but full as large or larger than our Jay mch of the Colour & shape of a Kings-fisher tho' not altogether so curiously Feath-erd, it has a large Crop. As I remember, there is a little Kings-fisher[8] much the same in every respect with ours.

If I mch mistake not I have seen both Gosse Hauk[9] & Falcon[10] besides there are several sorts of the lesser Kind of Stannels[11]

There is likewise the Kite[12] & the Ringtale[13]

I never heard the Cuckow there to my remembrance[14]

There's both a Brown Owle & White Owle[15] mch wt as large as a goose, wch often kills their hens & Poultry in the night, the

---

[6] Francis Willoughby (1635–1672), English ornithologist.

[7] Osprey, *Pandion haliaetus.*   [8] *Megaceryle alcyon* (not from McAtee).

[9] Goshawk, *Accipiter gentilis.*   [10] Peregrine falcon, *Falco peregrinus.*

[11] Small hawks, especially the kestrel, *Falco tinnunculus.*

[12] An unidentified falcon.   [13] Marsh hawk, *Circus cyaneus.*

[14] Both the yellow-billed cuckoo, *Coccyzus americanus,* and the black-billed cuckoo, *Coccyzus erythrophthalmus,* are found in Virginia today, but may be more common in the mountains than on the coast.

[15] The brown owl has not been identified, but the white was probably the snowy owl, *Nyctea scandiaca.*

white Owle is a very delicate featherd bird, all the feathers upon her brest & back being snow white, and tipd wth a punctal of jett black, besides there is a barne Owle[16] mch like ours & a little sort of Scritch Owle[17]

There's both the Raven[18] & the Carrion Crow[19] I doe not remember I ever saw any Rookes[20] there, Dr. Moulin & my selfe when we made our Anatomies together when I was at London we showd to the Royal Society[21] that all flat bild birds that groped for their meat had three pair of nerves that came down into their bills whereby as we conceived they had that acuracy to distinguish wt was proper for food & wt to be rejected by their tast when they did not see it and as this was most evident in a Ducks bill & head, I drawd a Cut thereof [see Plate III, facing p. 64] and left it in your custody, a Duck has larger Nerves that come into their bills than geese or any other bird that I have seen & therefore quafer & grope out their meat the most but I had then discoverd none of these Nerves in round billd birds but since in my Anatomies in the Country In a Rooke I first oberved two Nerves came down betwixt the eyes into the uper Bill but considerably smaler than any of the 3 pair of nerves in the bills of Ducks but larger than the Nerves in any other round bild birds & tis remarkable these birds more than any other round bild birds seeme to grope for their meat in Cow-dunge & the like   Since I have found in several round bild birds the like Nerves comeing down betwixt the eyes but so very small that had I not seen them first in a Rooke I should scarse have made the discovery, in the Lower bill there are nerves have mch wt the same Situation wth the flat

---

[16] *Tyto alba.*   [17] Screech owl, *Otus asio.*   [18] *Corvus corax.*
[19] *Corvus brachyrhynchos.*
[20] The rook is a European species, *Corvus frugilegus.*
[21] "Anatomical Observations in the heads of Fowel made at several times," by the late Allen Moulin, M.D., S.R.S., read before the Royal Society, February 1, 1687/8 (*Phil. Trans.*, XVII [1693], 711–16) .

bild birds but so very smal scarse discernable, unless to the cautious & curious.

The night Raven wch some call the Virginia Bat is about the biggness of a Cuckow featherd like them but very short, & short legd not discernable when it flies wch is only in the Evening scuding like our night Raven[22]

There's a great sort of ravanous bird that feeds upon Carrion as bigg very nigh as an Eagle wch they call a Turkie Bustard,[23] its feathers are of a duskish black, it has red gills resembling those of a Turkie whence it has its name, it is nothing of the same sort of bird wth our English Turkie bustard, but is rather a species of the Kites for it will hover on the wing somthing like them, & is carnivorous; the fat thereof dissolved into an oyle is recomended mightily agst old Aches & Sciatica pains.

I think there are no Jack daws, nor any Magg-pies, they there prize a Mag-pie as mch as we doe their Red bird[24]

The Pica Glandaria or Jay[25] is much less than our English Jay & of another colour for it is all blew where ours is brown the wings marbled as curiously as ours are, it has both the same Crie, & suddain Jetting motion.

There are great variety & curiosity in the Wood peckers there's one as bigg as our Magpie wth blackish brown feathers & a large scarlet tuft on the top of the head,[26] there are four or five sorts of wood Peckers more, variegated wth green, yellow & red heads   others spotted black & white most lovely to behold, there's a tradition amongst them, that the Tongue of one of these wood-Peckers dried will make the teeth drop out if pickd

---

[22] McAtee has identified this bird as the whippoorwill, *Caprimulgus vociferus,* but Clayton's description applies better to the nighthawk or bullbat, *Chordeiles minor.*

[23] *Cathartes aura.*   [24] Cardinal, *Richmondena cardinalis.*

[25] Blue jay, *Cyanocitta cristata.*

[26] Pileated woodpecker, *Hylatomus pileatus.*

therewth & cure the tooth ache <tho' I believe little of it but looke on it ridiculous> yet I thought fitt to hint as mch that others may trie for sometimes such old-stories refer to some peculiar virtues tho' not to all that is said of them.

There be wild Turkies[27] extreme large they talk of Turkies that have been killd that have weighd betwixt fifty & Sixty pound weight. The largest that ever I saw weighd somthing better than 38 pound they have very long leggs & will run prodigiously fast, I remember not that ever I saw any of them on the wing, except it were once their feathers are of a blackish shineing colour that in the Sun shine like a Doves neck very specious

Hens & Cocks are for the most part wthout tailes & rumps, & as some have assured me our English hens after some time being kept there have their rumps rot off.[28] Which I'me the apter to believe being all their hens are certainly of English breed I'me sorry I made no Anatomical observations thereof & remarks about the use of the Rumps in Birds wch at present I take to be a couple of glands containing a sort of juice for the Varnishing the feathers haveing observed all birds have mch recourse wth their bills to the Rumps when they dress their plumes whereby they scud through the Aire more nimbly in their flight.

Partridges[29] there are mch smaler than ours, & resort in Covies as ours doe; their flesh is very white & much excels ours in my mind sed de gustibus non est disputandum

Their Turtle Doves[30] are of a duskish blew colour mch less than our common pidgeon the whole traine is longer much than the tailes of our Pidgeons, the middle feather being the longest there's the strangest story of a vast number of these

[27] *Meleagris gallopavo.*   [28] This seems a bit hard to believe or explain.

[29] Bobwhite, *Colinus virginianus.*

[30] This seems to refer to the now extinct passenger pigeon, *Ectopistes migratorius.*

Pidgeons that came in a flock a few years before I came thither they say they came thro' New England New York & Virginia & were so prodigious in number as to darken the skie for several hours in the place over wch they flew, & broake massie bows where they light & many like things wch I have had assirted to me by many eye wittnesses of credit that to me it was wthout doubt the relaters being very sober persons & all agreeing in a story, nothing of the like ever happend since nor did I ever see past 10 in a flock together that I remember. I am not fond of such storys & had suppressed the relateing of it but that I have heard the same from very many.

The Thrush[31] & Feldifire[32] are much like ours, & are only seen in winter there accordingly as they are here.

Their Mocking Birds may be compared to our Singing Thrushes, being mch of the same biggness, there are two sorts, the gray[33] and the Redd,[34] the gray has feathers mch wt the colour of our gray plovers wth white in the Wings like a mag-Pie, this has the mch softer note & will imitate in its singing the notes of all birds that it hears & is accounted mch the finest singing bird in the world. Dr. Moulin & I made in our Anatomy many observations of singing Birds to this effect The Ears of birds differ mch from those of men or beasts, there's almost a direct passage from one eare to the other of Birds so that prick but the small membrane caled the Drum on either eare & water poured in at one eare, will run out at the other   But this is not all, but wt is mch more remarkable they have no Coclea but instead thereof there's a smal Cocleous or twisting passage that opens into a large cavity, that runs betwixt two Sculls & passes all round the head, the upper Scull is supported by many hundreds of small thred-like Pillers or Fibers wch as we supposed had another use also to breake the

[31] Not identified.   [32] Common robin, *Turdus migratorius.*
[33] *Mimus polyglottos.*   [34] Brown thrasher, *Toxostoma rufum.*

sound from makeing any confused Eccho, & to make it one & distinct this passage we observed betwixt the 2 Sculls was mch larger in Singing Birds than in others that doe not sing so very remarkable that any person that has been but showd this may easily judge by the head wt Bird is a singing bird or has an aptitude thereto tho' he never saw the bird before, nor knew wt bird it were this has often made me reflect how mch the modification of voices depends upon the acuracy of the eare & how deaf persons become dumb, & since I have observed that many Children that have an acute wit enough that are slow of Speech that is long before they speake are mch longer before they can pronounce those letters that are Sharps as g: h: r: & never have an aptitude to learne to sing. Hence I judge that Songs that have many Sharps in them are the difficultest to sing well & discover any person's skill upon the tryal of Musick most, This I suppose only, haveing no skill in musick myselfe nor haveing ever discoursed any person about it As I remember we showd some of these things to the Royal Society & I drew some Cutts thereof & gave the Dr upon promise that he would put these & many other our joynt observations in print but I heare he is since dead. I have Anatamoized most sorts of Creatures & neaver found any four-footed creature wth an eare like a bird unless a Mole & a Mole has an Eare mch like them wth a very thin double Scull, & great cavity like a bird & is very acute of hearing the Scull by reason of the large cavity is very slender & easily crushd so that a mole is quickly killd wth a bruise on the Scul like a Lark & upon the bruise the membrances of the Scul turne black whence Segerus[85] mistake Membranae Cerebri in supersicie exteriori omnino nigrae visae[36] but when I have taken care not to bruise the Scul the

[85] Not identified.
[36] Freely translated: the membranes of the brain on the outside appeared completely black.

membraines were not black at all   both Segerus & Severinus[37] I think had some perceptions of the different structure of a moles eare, but not anything of its analogy to a birds eare, they speake of a bone egregie pumicosum & Segerus says there's a ductus ad ossis usque petrosi cavitatem protensus, plurimis fibrillis membraneis annectabatur.[38]   but to return this mocking-bird haveing its name from mimicking all other birds in singing, is a wonderfull metled bird bold & brisk & yet seemes to be of a very tender constitution, neither Singing in Winter, nor in the midst of Summer & wth mch difficulty are any of them brought to live in England.

The Red mocking is of a duskish red, or rather brown, it sings very well, but has not so soft a note as the Gray mocking bird.

Virginy Nightingale, or Red Bird   there are 2 sorts   the Cocks of both sorts are of a pure Scarlet the Hens of a Duskish Red   I distinguish them into two sorts, for the one has a tufted cops on the head, the other is smooth featherd.   I never saw a tufted Cock wth a smooth headed hen, or on the Contrary; they generaly resorting a Cock & hen together;[39] & play in a thicket of Thorns or Bryers in the Winter nigh to which the boys set their traps & so catch them & sell them to the Merchants for about 6d apiece by whom they are brought for England   they are somthing less than a thrush.

There's a Bird very injurious to Corn, they call a Blackbird; I look on it a sort of Starling for they crie somthing like them but doe not sing, are mch wt of the same biggness, have flesh blackish like theirs, they resort in great flocks together   they

[37] Marco Aurelio Severino, an eminent Italian physician, born in Calabria in 1580. He became a professor of anatomy and medicine at Naples and published a number of professional works. He died in 1656.

[38] Roughly: a bone much like pumice stone; and: Segerus says there's a hollow passage extending right up to the bones of the petrous [temporal bone containing the inner ear] connected by a great number of membrane fibers.

[39] Clayton seems to be distinguishing between the cardinal, *Richmondena cardinalis,* and the summer tanager, *Piranga rubra.*

are as black as a crow all over their bills & all only some of them have scarlet feathers in the pinions of their wings   quaere whether a distinct species.[40]

They have a lark nothing differing from our common Lark,[41]   They have another Bird wch they call a Lark that is mch larger, as bigg as a Starling, it has a soft note, feeds on the ground & as I remember has the specifical Character of a long heele, it is more enclined to yellow & has a large halfe moone on its brest of yellow   if it have not a long heele, quaere, whether a species of the Yellow-hammer.[42]

They have a Martin very like only larger than ours that builds after the same manner.[43]   The honourble Coll. Bacon[44] has remarked for several years that they constantly come thither upon the tenth of March one or two of them appearing before being seene hovering in the Aire for a day or two then goe away & as he supposed returnd wth the great flock   The Coll. delighted mch in this bird & made like pidgeon holes at the end of his house wth boards purposely for them.

Their Swallow differs but little from ours.[45]

They have a bird they call a blew bird[46] of a curious azure Colour about the biggness of a Chafinch.

[40] Clayton was correct in suspecting that the red-winged blackbird, *Agelaius phoeniceus*, might be a species distinct from the other blackbirds which he had observed.   It is not possible to identify the latter from his description. The starling was introduced from England many years later.

[41] Not identified.

[42] This was certainly the eastern meadowlark, *Sturnella magna*.   Present-day bird books also list the flicker or yellowhammer under the heading of "similar species."

[43] *Progne subis*.

[44] Nathaniel Bacon, Sr., first cousin of Nathaniel Bacon, Jr., the "Rebel."

[45] McAtee considered this to be the barn swallow, *Hirundo rustica erythrogaster*, but a number of swallows seem to be possible.

[46] Eastern bluebird, *Sialia sialis*.   Although McAtee makes no such suggestion, this might possibly have been an indigo bunting, *Passerina cyanea*, which is slightly smaller than the bluebird.   The males are a markedly rich blue all over, much more striking than a bluebird's blue, which would answer Clayton's description of "azure."

There be other sorts of Goldfinches variegated wth red Orange & yellow feathers, very specious & beautifull.[47]

Sparrows not mch different from the English but build not in the Eaves of houses that ever I saw.[48]

The Snow bird[49] wch I take to be mch the same wth our hedge Sparrow this is so caled because it seldom appears about houses but agst snow or very cold weather.

The Humming Bird that feeds upon the hony of flowers[50] I have been told by some persons that they have kept of these humming birds alive & fed them wth water & sugar, they are mch the smallest of all birds have long bills & curious coloured feathers but differ mch in Colour.

Hearons 3 or 4 several sorts, one larger than the English, featherd mch like a Spanish goose.[51]

Another sort that only comes in Summer milk white with red leggs very lovely to behold.[52]

The Bittern is there less than in England & does not make that sounding noise that ever I heard.[53]

Curlews somthing less than our English tho' bigger than a Wimbrel.[54]

---

[47] McAtee did not attempt to identify the birds Clayton included in this group, but no doubt one of them was the common American goldfinch, *Spinus tristis.*

[48] The English sparrow or house sparrow, *Passer domesticus,* was introduced long after Clayton's time and is not closely related to our many native sparrows.

[49] Slate-colored junco, *Junco hyemalis.*

[50] Ruby-throated hummingbird, *Archilochus colubris.* Durand remarked of this bird that it was "no larger than a big fly with feathers the colors of the rainbow. This little animal feeds on dew & the juice of fragrant flowers & smells so sweet that Englishmen who came here, I was told, had them dressed & dried in an oven to sell later in England for as much as eight pounds sterling apiece, because of their sweet odor" (*A Huguenot Exile,* p. 124).

[51] Great blue heron, *Ardea herodias.*   [52] Not identified.

[53] The American bittern, *Botaurus lentiginosus,* does make a "noise" or song.

[54] Hudsonian curlew, *Numenius phaeopus hudsonicus.*

The sandpiper mch resembling the English.[55]

The Snipe two sorts one mch resembling ours the other mch less.[56]

The tewitts[57] are smaller than the English & have no long toppins but just like a young one that begins to flie.

There are great numbers of Wild Swans.[58]

Wild-geese[59] & Brent geese[60] all winter in mighty flocks, Wild Ducks innumerable Teale[61] Wigeon[62] Sheldrakes[63] Virginia Didapers[64] the Black-Diver[65] etc.

In my return home for England, May 1686, off of the Banks of New found Land when we were according to account, a hundred Leagues from the Shoare, we saw several prodigious floating Islands of Ice, no less to our wonder than Terror, for they were very dangerous: I got the Master to saile one day as nigh one of them as we securely durst, which we judged to be full a League in Length & was higher above water than the top of our Main-mast, the snow drove toe & fro upon it as upon a large plane, there was a great flock of smal black divers[66] that were not mch bigger than a Feldifire came to us a little before but all of them then left and betooke themselves to this Island

---

[55] Spotted sandpiper, *Actitis macularia.*

[56] The first was probably the common or Wilson's snipe, *Capella gallinago delicata,* and the other is unidentified.

[57] The common lapwing, pewit (tewit), or bastard plover, *Vanellus cristatus,* of England and Europe. Not identified by McAtee.

[58] The whistling swan, *Cygnus columbianus,* and the trumpeter swan, *Cygnus buccinator.*

[59] The most common goose on the Atlantic Coast today is the Canada goose, *Branta canadensis,* but others are found.

[60] Common brant, *Branta bernicla.*

[61] Both the green-winged teal, *Anas carolinensis,* and the blue-winged teal, *Anas discors,* are found in Virginia today.

[62] American widgeon or baldpate, *Mareca americana.*

[63] Mergansers. Three species are found in Virginia today. These are the hooded merganser, *Lophodytes cucullatus;* the American merganser, *Mergus merganser americanus;* and the red-breasted merganser, *Mergus serrator.*

[64] Grebes, according to McAtee. Several species are found in Virginia today.

[65] Probably the common loon, *Gavia immer.*   [66] Dovekie, *Plautus alle.*

of Ice they dived the constantlyst, and the longest at a time of any bird that I ever saw. We saw as I remember nigh thirty of these Islands of Ice. Capt. Rider[67] being some few days later in his passage & beareing more to the Nore told me he saw many more of these Islands of Ice & some mch larger.

There are in Virginia a great many Cormorants[68] Several sorts of Gulls[69] & in & about the bay many Gannets.[70]

Thus much for the Birds.

> I am your most assured friend & humble
> Servt
>
> J Clayton

Wakefield Nover 24
  1693

[67] Unidentified.

[68] The most common cormorant of the Atlantic Coast today is the double-crested cormorant, *Phalacrocorax auritus,* but the European cormorant, *Phalacrocorax carbo,* is occasionally found as far south as Virginia.

[69] A number of species of gulls are found in Virginia today.

[70] *Moris bassana.* This appeared as "Bannet" in *Phil. Trans.*

XI

"SEVEN SEVERALL SORTS
OF SNAKES – AND VIPERS MOST DEADLY"[1]

There were neither Horses, Bulls, Cows, Sheep, or Swine, in all the Country, before the comeing of the English; as I have heard, & have mch reason to believe.[2] But, now amongst the English inhabitants there are good store of horses, though they are very negligent, & careless, about the breed; it is true there is a Law, that no horse shall be kept stoned under a certain size,[3] but it is not put in execution. Such as they are, there are good store, & cheape or cheaper than in England, worth about five pounds a piece. They never shoe them,[4] nor stable them, in general; some few gentlemen may be somthing more curious, but it is very rare; yet they ride pretty sharply, a planters pace is a Proverb, wch is a good sharp hand gallop. The Indians have not yet learnd to ride, only the King of Pomon-

[1] Taken from the manuscript in the Archives of the Royal Society of London, Classified Papers C 2.23/1–11. Appended to the end of the account of the beasts is Clayton's second letter to Waller (see p. 122, below). On the back of this is the following notation: "Do to Do Containing an account of the Beasts and Reptiles of Virginia Wakefield May 22:1694 Read June 6:1694 Entd. L. B. Suppl. pr Trans. 210." The title is from the entry made in the Journal Book of the Royal Society, VI (1690–96), 241. The letter was printed in *Phil. Trans.* XVIII (1694), 121–35.

[2] Horses are thought to have died out in the New World during the Pleistocene and to have been reintroduced by the Spanish in Florida.

[3] The law required that small horses be castrated (Hening, *Statutes,* II, 36).

[4] Shoeing was considered unnecessary because of the sandy soil and scarcity of rocks in Tidewater Virginia.

kie[5] had got 3 or 4 horses for his own saddle, & an attendant, wch I think should in no wise be indulged, for I looke on the allowing them horses mch more dangerous than even guns & pouder.

Wild Bulls, & *Cows,* there are now in the uninhabited parts, but such only as have been bred from some that have strayd, & become wild, & have propogated their kind, & are difficult to be shott, haveing a great acuteness of smelling. The common rate of a Cow, & Calfe, is 50s, sight unseene, be she bigg, or little, they are never very curious to examine that point.

Their *Sheep* are of a midling size, pretty fine fleeced in general, & most persons of Estate begin to keep flocks, which hitherto has not been mch regarded, because of the Wolves that destroy them[6] so that a piece of mutton is a finer Treat, than either Venison, wild-goose, Duck, Wigeon, or Teale.

Elke, I have heard of them beyond the inhabitants, & that there was one presented to Sr. Wm. Berkley,[7] wch he somtimes kept.

Deare, there are abundance of brave red Deare, so that a good woodsman as they call them, will keep a house wth Venison, the Indians they say make artificial sorts of heads of bows of trees wch they consecrate to their gods, & these they put on to deceive the deare when they goe a shooting, or hunting, as they call it, & by mimiking the feeding of the Deare they by degrees get wthin shot.

Swine, they have now in great abundance Shoats, or Pork-

---

[5] The Pamunkeys, a large tribe, lived on the peninsula formed by the Pamunkey and Mattaponi rivers, in the vicinity of present-day West Point, Virginia.

[6] Some years previously the settlers had given cows to the Indians as bounty for wolves' heads, with the dual objective of reducing the wolf population and "civilizing" the Indians by making them property owners (Morton, *Colonial Virginia,* I, 216).

[7] Sir William Berkeley (1608–77) was twice governor of Virginia, 1642–52 and 1660–76.

rels, are their general food. And I believe as good as any Westphalia certainly far exceeding our English.

Rackoone I take it to be a species of a monkie, somthing less than a ffox, gray haird, its feet formed like a hand, & the face too has likewise the resemblance of a Monkies, besides being kept tame, they are very Apish, they are very prejudicial to their poultry, as I remember.

An *Opossom* as bigg, & somthing shaped like our Badgers, but of a lighter dun colour, wth a long tale somthing like a rat, but as thick as a mans Thumb, the Skin of its belly is very large, & folded so as to meet like a purse, wherein they secure their young whilst little, & tender, wch will as naturaly run thither as chickins to a hen, in this false bellys they will carry their young, these also feed on, & devour corn.[8]

Hares, many will have them to be a hedge Rabbet, but I know not wht they meane thereby. I take them to be a perfect Species of hares, because I have seene Leverets[9] there wth the white spott in the head, wch the old ones have not, so it is in England; & the downe is perfectly the Colour of our hairs, they sit as our haires doe & make no holes & borrows in the earth, true they are but about the biggness of an English Rabbet, & no faster,[10] they generally take into some hollow tree wthin a little Space, wch then the people catch by gathering the witherd leaves, & seting them on fire wthin the hollow of the tree, & smoakeing of them so till they fall down, Somtimes they take long bryers, & twist them in the down, & Skin, & so pull them forth.

---

[8] This unfamiliar animal was something of a sensation in English scientific circles for a long time. As late as February 3, 1742, Peter Collinson read Dr. John Mitchell's "Account of the O'possum" before the Royal Society of London (Journal Book, XVIII, 32).

[9] Rabbits under a year old.

[10] Rabbits differ from other hares in their burrowing habits and in their hairless young.

Squirrels, there are 3 sorts. The 1st is the great ffox Squir-rel,[11] mch larger than the English, & gray, almost as a common Rabbet. These are very common, I have eaten of them at the best Gentlemens Tables, & they are good as a Rabbet. The 2d is the flying Squirrel, of a lighter dun colour, & less mch than the English Squirrel, the Skin on either side the belly extended is very large; betwixt the fore legg & hind legg, wch helps them mch in their skiping from one bough to another, that they will leap farther than the fox Squirrel, though mch less, yet this is still rather skiping than flieing though I think the distinction well enough – .[12] The 3d is the Ground Squirrel.[13] I never saw any of this sort, only I have been told of them, & have had thus described to me, to be little bigger than a mouse, finely spotted like a young fawn by wt I further apprehended they are an absolute sort of Dore-mouse[14] only different in Colour.

Musk Rats,[15] in all things shaped like our Water Rats,[16] only somthing larger, & is an absolute species of Water Rats, only haveing a curious musky sent, I kept one for a certain time in a wood chest. 2 days before it died it was extrordinary odorifer-ous & sented the roome very mch, but the day that it died, & a day the sent was very smal, yet afterwards the skin was very fragrant, the stones also smeld very well. They build houses as Beavers doe, in the Marshes, & Swamps <as they there call them> by the Water Sides, wth 2 or 3 ways into them, & they are finely daubed wthin, I puld one in pieces purposely to see the Contrivance, there were 3 different Lodgeing Rooms, very neat, one higher than another, as I conceive purposely made

---

[11] *Sciurus niger,* whose habitat is the southern pinelands. Clayton may have been confusing the fox squirrel with the common gray squirrel, *Sciurus carolinensis.*

[12] A squirrel of the genus *Glaucomys.*   [13] Chipmunks.

[14] Small European rodents of the family Muscardinidae.

[15] *Ondatra zibethica.*   [16] *Arvicola amphibius.*

for retirement, when the Water rises higher than ordinary, they are considerably large, haveing mch Trash & Lumbre to make their houses wthall, I suppose they live mostly on fish.

Batts, as I remember at least 2 sorts, one a large sort wth long eares, & particularly long stragling hairs. The other mch like the English somthing larger I think, very common.[17]

I never heard of any *Lions,* they told me of a Creature kild whilst I was there, in Gloster County, wch I conceived to be a sort of Pard[18] or Tyger.

Beares there are, And yet but few in the Inhabited part of Virginia; toward Carolina there are many more. There was a smal Beare kild wthin 3 miles of James City the yeare that I left the Country, but it was supposed to have strayd, & swame over James River. They are not very fierce, their flesh is commended for a very ritch sort of Pork, but the lying side of the Beare, as I remember is but halfe the Value of the other, weight for Weight.[19]

There are several sorts of *Wild Catts,* & *Poll Catts.*[20]

Beavers build their houses in like manner as the Musk Rats doe, only mch larger, & wth pieces of timber make dammes over Rivers. As I suppose, either to preserve their furrs drie in their passage over the Rivers, otherwise to catch fish by standing to watch them thereon, & jumping upon them on a suddain, they are very subtil Creatures, & if halfe of the stories be true that I have been told,[21] they have a very orderly government amongst them, in their works each knows his

[17] Several species of bats are found in Virginia today. These include the little brown bat, *Myotis lucifugus;* the large brown bat, *Eptisicus fuscus;* and the red bat, *Lasiurus borealis.*

[18] An old word for leopard, possibly a cougar, *Felis concolor.*

[19] The black bear, *Euarctos americanus,* is still fairly common in the Dismal Swamp and in mountainous areas of Virginia.

[20] Bobcat, *Lynx ruffus,* and skunk, one of the species of *Mephitis.*

[21] He seems to have heard a lot of tall tales and to have had little first-hand acquaintance with the beaver.

proper work, & station, & the overseers beat those young ones that loiter in their business, & will make them crie, & work stoutly.

Wolves, there are great store, you may heare a company hunting in an Evening, & yelping, like a pack of beagles, but they are very cowardly, & dare scarse venture on any thing that faces them, yet if hungry will pull down a good large shep that flies from them.   I never heard that any of them adventured to set on man or child.

Foxes, they are very mch like ours, only their fur is mch more grizeld, or gray, neither doe I remember ever to have seene any fox holes, but of this I am not positive.

Every house keeps 3 or 4 mungril *Doggs* to destroy virmin, such as Wolves, ffoxes, Racoones, Opossoms, etc.   But they never hunt wth hounds, I suppose, because there are so many branches of rivers that they cannot follow them.[22]   Neither doe they keep Grey-hounds, because they say that they are subject to breake their necks by runing agst Trees, & any Cur will serve to run their haires into a hollow tree, where after the aforesd manner they Catch them.

They have great store both of Land & Water Tortoises, but they are very smal   I think I never say any in that Country, to exceed a foot in Length; there is also another sort of Land Tortoise, different from the common sort, wth a higher ridged back, and speckled wth red sort of Spotts.

Froggs they have of Several Sorts, One of a prodigious largness, eight or so times as bigg as any in England, & it makes a strange noise, somthing like the Bellowing of a Bull, or betwixt that, & the hollow Sounding noise that the English Bittern makes.

[22] Either Clayton was mistaken, or the practice was introduced soon after this, for his namesake, John Clayton the botanist, describing hunting in Virginia in 1738, said, "Some hunt the foxes with hounds as you do in England" (*Va. Mag. Hist. Biog.,* VII [1899], 172–74) .

Another very common sort wch they call toads, because black, but I think differs nothing from our black frogg, they have toades also like ours in England. And another Small sort of Frogg, wch makes a noise like pack horse bells all the Spring long. Another little green frogg, that will leap prodigiously, wch they therefore call the flying frogg. There is frequently heard in the woods a shrill sort of noise, mch like that wch our Shrew Mouse makes, but mch sharper, I could never learne the certainty wt it was that made this noise, it is generaly in a tree, & some have asserted to me, that it was made by the green frogg,[23] yet I scarsely believe it. Mr. Banister assured me it was made by a sort of *Scarabeus* Beetle[24] that is I think full as bigg as the huming bird, but neither doe I believe that, & for this reason, for I never saw that beetle so low as the Salts, but always as high up in the Country as the freshes, & that noise is frequent all over the Country.

Lizards, that are gray, very common, the Snakes feed mch on them, for I have taken Several of them out of the bellys of Snakes.

Snakes about 7 Several Sorts. The Rattle Snake so caled from certain rattles at the end of the tale. These Rattles seeme like so many perishd joints, being a drie Husk over certain joints, & the common opinion is, that there are as many Rattles or joints, as the Snake is yeares old. I killd 4 or 5 & they had each Eleven, Twelve or Thirteen joints each, but the young ones have no rattles of a yeare, or two, but they may be known notwthstanding, Being very regularly diced or checkerd, black & gray, on the backs: The old shake & shiver these rattles wth wonderfull nimbleness when they are any ways disturbed, their bite is very deadly, yet not always of the same force, but more or less mortal accordingly as the Snake is in

[23] The tree frog, one of the species of *Hyla*.
[24] Probably the cicada, *Tibicen pruinosa*.

force or vigour, & therefore in June or July mch worse, & more
mortal, than in March & April;[25]   This Snake is a very majes-
tick sort of creature, & will scarse meddle wth any thing unless
provoked, but if any thing offend it, it makes directly at them.
I was told a pleasant Story of an old Gentleman Coll. Cleyborn
as I remember was his name, the same that sent the Rattle
snakes to the Royal Society, some years since.[26]   He had an odd
fancy of keeping some of these Snakes always in Barrells in the
house, & one time an Indian pretending that he could charme
them, so as to take them by the neck in his hand wthout biting
of him; the old gentleman caused a Rattle snake to be brought
forth, the Indian began his charme wth a little wand, whisking
it round & Round the Rattle snakes head, bringing it by
degrees higher & nigher, & at length flung the Switch away &
whisked his hand about in like maner, bringing his hand
nigher still & nigher, by takeing less circles, when the Old
Gentleman imediately hitt the Snake wth his crutch, & the
Snake snapd the Indian by the hand, & bote him very sharply
betwixt the fingers, wch put his charme to an end, & he roared
out; but stretchd his arme out as high as he could, calleing for a
string, wherewth he bound his arme as hard as possibly he
could, & clapd a hot burning cole thereon, & singed it stoutly,
whereby he was cured, but looked pale a long while after.   & I
believe this truly one of the best ways in the world of cureing
the bite either of viper or Madd Dogg.   I was with the
Honoble Sqre Boyle, when he made certain experimts of
cureing the bite of Vipers, wth certain East India Snake
stones,[27] that were sent him by King James the 2d, the Queene,
& some of the nobility, purposely to have him trie their virtue,

---

[25] Questionable.

[26] William Claiborne (c.1587–1677), member of the Council and secretary of
state.

[27] Sometimes called Goa stones.   Robert Boyle defined them as stony excretions "that are said to be found in the heads of a certain kind of serpents about
Goa, and some other Eastern countries" (Birch, *Boyle,* V, 127).

& efficacy: for that end he got some brisk Vipers, & made them bite the thighs of certain pullets, & the brests of others, he applyd nothing to one of the pullets, & it died wthin 3 minutes & a halfe as I remember; but I think they all recoverd to wch he applyd the Snake-stones, though they turned wonderfull pale, their combs etc. imediately, & they became extreame sick, & purged wthin halfe an hour, & the next morning all their flesh was turned greene to a wonder, never the less they recoverd by degrees, the manner of the application was only by laying on the stone, & by two cross bitts of a very sticking Diatulum plaster[28] binding it on, wch he let not lie on past an hour or two, but I think not so long, tooke the stone off, & put it into milk for some time. Some stones were of mch stronger virtue than others.[29] I proposed a piece of unquentchd lime stone to be applyd, & see whether it might not prove as powerfull, but know not whether ever it was tried, but here on telling Mr. Boyle the story of this Indian, he approved the method of cure, & sd an actual cautery was the most certain cure.[30] The Poison both of Viper, & Mad-Dogg <as I conceive> kill by thickning of the blood, after the manner that Runnet congeals milk when they make cheese.[31] Vipers & all the Viperous brood, as Rattle Snakes, etc. that are deadly have I believe their poisonous teeth fistulous,[32] for so I have observed the Vipers teeth are, & the Rattle Snake's very re-

[28] An adhesive plaster made by boiling lead oxide, olive oil, and water together and spreading the mixture on sheets of linen.

[29] No reference to this particular experiment has been found in Boyle's works, except for the following statement: "And this same experience of my own made with a genuine stone of this kind, upon the bodies of brutes, much inclines me to give credit to it" (Birch, *Boyle*, V, 128).

[30] Boyle does not seem to mention Clayton definitely by name in this connection, but it may be that he refers to him when speaking of rattlesnakes: "of which I remember a learned eye-witness, that lived divers years in *Virginia*, where they much abound, related to me a very strange instance, which I cannot now stay to set down" (Birch, *Boyle*, V, 80).

[31] The venom of different types of snakes acts variously.

[32] Hollow.

markable, & therefore they kill so very speedily by injecting the poison through those fistulous teeth into the very mass of blood, but the bite of Madd Doggs is oft of Long continuance before it get into & corrupt the Mass of blood, being it sticks only to the out sides of the teeth, & therefore when they bite through any thickness of cloaths, it rarely proves mortal, the cloaths wipeing the poison off, before it come to the flesh. A girle that was bitt about New Years day, continued well till Whitsontide, when comeing to see certain friends in our parts, she fell very ill, and being a poore girle they came to me, it pleasd God I recoverd her. Somtime after she returned to give me thanks for saveing her life, being two persons that were bitt wth the same Dogg were dead whilst she was under cure, & therefore she was the fullyer convinced she owed her life to me, but of this I shall give a more particular instance by & by. But the Poisons of Vipers seemes to be like the injecting of liquors into the Veins of creatures, Dr. Moulin & I made many experiments of this nature together, & I have made many more by myselfe.[33] We once I remember injected halfe a dram of Allom into the Jugular veine of a dogg before the Royal Society, the Allom being only dissolved in a little Water, wch wthin somthing less than one minutes time was so absolutely dead as not to have the least convulsive motion, & I have done the like wth many other things, besides Allom, but wth som-things it is more curdled & broaken than wth others, & will differ mch both as to colour & consistence. Salt Petre kills mch wt as quickly as Allom, but then the blood in the hart lookes very florid, smooth, & Even. I wish some Person of observa-tion & leasure would prosecute these sorts of experimt, & make injections of the several things most used in Physik into the

[33] Moulin gave a paper on this subject, "An Account of an Experiment of the Injection of Mercury into the Blood, and its ill Effects on the Lungs" (*Phil. Trans.*, XV [1690/1], 486).

veins of creatures both in different quantitys, & into different veins, as into the thigh veins of some doggs, & Jugulars of others, & in mch lesser quantitys of such things as kill suddenly, for in the little time I have spent in these sorts of experiment, I easily perceive notable discoverys might be made thereby; one Dogg that lived became lame, & gouty; another wth quicksilver died, in some 16 weekes time, Consumptive, & I discovered quicksilver in the impostumated[34] parts of his Lungs. Quaere whether some persons that have beene fluxd, or used Quicksilver oyntmts, & the like, & afterwards become consumptive, owe not their distemper to the abusive use of a most excellent remedy, much after the same manner, the subtile quicksilver geting into the Mass of blood by degrees through its ponderosity settles in the lobes of the Lunges, & causes ulcers there. but to return. The poison of Vipers, & Mad doggs I suppose kill by thickning of the blood, as many malignant feavers also doe; in all wch cases, I looke on Volatile Salts to be the properst physik, as keepeing the blood from congealeing. I had a singular instance hereof in a Gentleman of Yorkshire, bitt wth a Greyhound on the Thursday, not 3 minutes before the Dogg died mad, he bitt him in several places of the hands, as he was giveing him a remedy, the Munday following the Gentleman was very ill, came to our Town to an Apothecary, his acquaintance, who knowing not wt to doe, desired my assistance, when I came, the Gentleman could talk, but evry 2 or 3 minutes he had violent fitts, & would tell us when it was over, that his brains worked like birme in an Ale fatt,[35] & seemed to froth up at evry fitt. The Apothecary had no volatile Salt of Vipers.[36] So I tooke the Volatile Salt of Am-

[34] Ulcerated.

[35] Barm (barme) was the froth which forms on the top of fermenting liquors, and ale-fat meant an ale vat.

[36] This has not been identified. The flesh of vipers was believed to have curative powers, so this was probably something extracted therefrom.

ber,[37] orderd him 10 Grains in Treacle water[38] evry halfe hour, he told me evry dose seemed to cleare his braine, & coole it, as perfectly as if a bason of cold water were pourd on his head, but it returnd by degrees again, haveing then a Volatile Salt by me that Vomits very well I gave him a dose thereof; it worked very well, & he was very mch better after it, I then orderd him to continue the volatile Salt of Amber once evry 4 hours, & at each 2 hours end, that is betwixt Spec Pleres Archonticon & Rue pouderd ana grains 15[39] whereby he was so well recoverd, that wthin 2 days he would needs goe home, to looke after some urgent affaires, & afterwards found himselfe so well, that he forgot to returne, & perfect the course, & I heard no more of him of halfe a yeare; When I was fetchd one morning to him in great hast, He had beene abroad, playd the good fellow, & in his returne home haveing road a great days journey, being weary, & I suppose finding himselfe indisposed, he stayd all night in our Town, it being fortunatly in his way. In the morning when he should have got up he could not stand, whereupon the Apothecary was sent for, & a Surgeon to blood him, wch was accordingly done, but he grew worse, for in this case I looke upon blooding to be very prejudicial, as well as in most malignant feavers, for thereby the Spirits are diminshd, & the blood congeald the sooner, when they had done all they could and the Symptoms still increased, they at length sent for me. I never saw man or creature *in that agonie* in all my life, that I found him in, senseless, & mad, when at best, but evry minute the fiercest Shiverings ran through him, his eyes would first Roll, & then set, as if ready to start out of his head, but above all the

[37] The distillation of amber yielded both the salt and the oil of amber, which also had medicinal uses.

[38] The word "treacle" can mean molasses, but this reference was probably to a water extract of English treacle, or creeping germander, *Teucrium chamaedrys*.

[39] Not identified.

swelling & luctation at his brest, as if he would burst, wch went of[f] wth a prodigious Sigh, all this I judge the effects of the hart labouring to discharge itselfe of the stagnateing blood, & the nervous convulsions as consequences thereof. & I'me the more confirmd in this, from wt I saw in a Woman that was bitt also wth a mad Dogg in the Legg, & fell ill the very day that she had paid the Chirugeon for her cure, & notwthstanding all that could be done, growing worse, they sent for me, I went & found her wth wt is caled a hydrophobia, She would looke earnestly after drink or Water, & seeme to desire it, but as soone as she began to drink, away it went be it wt it would, wth the greatest violence she could possibly fling it. I gave her the vomit hereafter & also before mentioned, but she got but little of it downe, & I had no more wth me, nevertheless it so brought her to her selfe that she could answer questions, & I asked her whether she was afraid of the drink & Water, when she flung the Cups in that violent maner from her. She sd No. but when she offerd to drink her brest & hart would not let her. I asked whether through any aversion or feare. She said, No. She was very thirsty but when she offerd to drink it struck to her hart, & stoped her breath. That is as I apprehend, the cold drink passing downe the throat struck a chillyness in the blood & made it readyer to stagnate, besides the very Act of drinking, hindring the free breathing conduced also much thereto, & therefore the hart was so suddenly oppressd that she could not forbear flinging away wtever she had in her hand. She complained also of a great rigor & stiffness or straitness of the Muscles of her brest, so that possible the Spiritous liquor that flows in the Genus Nervosum[40] may be congealed as well as the blood, or the same effects may be supposed notwthstanding to be the result of the condensed blood clogging both the hart & Lungs, so that the brest may seeme to be straitend therewth.

[40] The nervous system.

The same I judge to be the cause of all the violent Luxations in this Gentleman, whose fingers I looked on, & found the places where he had formerly been bitt, turnd blackish, & mch inflamed about them, wch confirmd me in my sentiment, that it was a relapse of his former distemper, that is of the bite of the Mad Dogg; I told them if any thing in the world would save his life, I judged it must be the former Vomit of Volatile Salts; they could not tell wt to doe, nevertheless such is the malignancy of the world, that as soone as it was given, they ran away & left me, saying he was now certainly a dead man to have a vomit given in that condition. Nevertheless it pleasd God, that he shortly after cried this fellow in the black has done me good, & after the first vomit, came so to himselfe, as to know us all. I vomited him evry other day wth this vomit for 3 times, & made him in the Interim to take Volatile Salt of Amber, & the aforesd pouders, & to wash his hands, & sores in a strong Salt brine, to drink Posset drink[41] wth Sage & Rue, & by this course, & the blessing of God, his life was saved, & he perfectly cured, for it is now four years since & he has had no relapse, I have cured several others by the Same method. Coll. Spencer the Secretary of State in Virginia, a very serious, & ingenious Gentleman, told me that his Servt brought him word once that a Sow haveing farrowd, a Rattle Snake was got into the den, & had killd the Piggs. The Coll. went to see the snake, wch they sd was still coyld in the Den, there followd them 2 or 3 mungrill Currs, & they set one of the Doggs at the Snake, wch was too quick for the Dogg, & snapt him by the Nose, whereupon he set a howling & ran immediately into the adjacent River, & died very shortly. Another of the Doggs upon the like attempt was bitt by the Snake also, & fell a howleing, & froathing, & tumbling, but being he died not so soone as the other dogg did, they fetchd some of the Herb wch

[41] Sour milk.

they call Dittany,[42] as haveing a great traditionary virtue for the cure of poisons, they pounded it, & adding a little water expressd the juice, & gave the Dogg frequently thereof, nevertheless he died wthin a day or two, the howleing of the Doggs he supposed gave notice to the Sow, & made her come furiously bristling, & run immediately into her Den, but being likewise bitt by the Snake, she set up a terrible Squeake, & ran also into the River, & there died. A Gentlewoman that was a notable female Doctress told me that a neighbour being bitt by a Rattle Snake swelld excessively, some days afterwards she was sent for, who found him swelld beyond wt she thought it had beene possible for the skin to containe & very thirsty. She gave him Oriental Bezoar[43] shaved, wth a strong Decoction of the aforesd Dittany, whereby she recovered the Person, to the best of my remembrance it was she that told me, asking him afterwards wt he felt when the snake first bote him, he sd, it seemed as if a flash of fire had ran through his veins; besides the Rattle Snake – – – There is the Blowing Snake,[44] an absolute Species of a Viper, but larger than any that I have seene in Europe, it is so caled, because it seemes to blow, & spread its head, & swell very mch before it bite, wch is very deadly, it is remarkable there is none of their snakes there, make any of that hissing noise that ours in England make, but only shoot out their tongues, shakeing them as ours doe wthout any noise at all, this is a short thick sort of Snake – – – There is another sort of deadly Snake, caled the Red Snake,[45] I once narrowly escaped treading on the back of one of them; they are of an ugly dark brown colour, inclined to red, their bellys are of a more duskie white, wth a large streake of Virmilion Red on

[42] See pp. 31–32.

[43] Excretions found in the alimentary tracts of ruminants.

[44] The harmless American puff adder or hog-nosed snake, *Heterodon platyrhinos.*

[45] Perhaps the copperhead, *Agkistrodon contortrix.*

either side, this too is of the Viper kind, but is not so short but its tale is more taper & small – – – – – The Horne Snake is as they say another sort of deadly snake, I never saw any of them unless once, shortly after my Arrival in that Country, wch I cannot attest to be the horne Snake, for I could not distinctly view it, being in a thicket of Sumach, it was pearched up about 2 foot high in a Sumach branch, its taile twisted about the Shrub, & about a quarter of a yard stood bolt forward, leaneing over the forked branch thereof. I could not see the horne, wch they say it has in its front, wherewth it strikes, & if it wound, is as deadly as the Rattle Snakes bite. The Gentleman that was wth me told me it was a horne Snake, but being in hast, & on horse back, & the Snake in a thicket, I could not see the horne,[46] but I had thought, I should never have seene more of them, I should have tooke a little pains to have beene better satisfied, this I think may not improperly be refered to the Dart Snakes.[47]

The Black Snake, is the largest I think of all others, but I'me sure the most common, I have killd several of them full six foot long, their bite is not deemed mortall, but it Swells, & turns to a runing Sore, they feed upon Lizards, Mice, Ratts, froggs, & toades, wch I have taken out of their bellys. I was once a Simpling[48] in the woods, on a faire Sun shine day, when I saw a Snake crawling on a tree that was fallen, & licking wth its forked tongue as it moved, I stood still to observe it, & saw it lick up small insects and flies, wth wonderfull nimbleness, catching them betwixt the forks of its tongue.

The Corn-Snake[49] most like the Rattle Snake of all others in

[46] There seems to be no snake known as the horn snake in Virginia today. There is a horned viper in Africa, *Cerastes cornutus,* and a nose-horned viper in Europe, *Vipera ammodytes.*

[47] Snakelike lizards of the genus *Acontias.* One of the examples of this term in the *Oxford English Dictionary* is quoted from Clayton.

[48] Collecting medicinal plants.   [49] *Coluber guttatus.*

Colour, but the Checkers are not so regular, neither has it any Rattles: they are most frequent in the Corn fields, & thence I suppose so caled, the Bite is not so venemous as the black Snakes.

The Water Snake,[50] a Smal Snake, I never saw any of them above a yard long, though I have somtimes seene 40 or 50 at once, they are of an ugly dark blackish colour, they say they are the least Venemous of any.

[50] The water moccasin or cottonmouth, *Agkistrodon piscivorus,* is quite venemous. Clayton probably refers to harmless snakes of the genus *Natrix.*

XII

"THE SPRING OF THE AIR
SEEMES TO BE GOVERNED BY HEAT"

[Second Letter to Waller][1]

Sir, Since the Royal Society has done me that honor, as to receive my imperfect Relations of Virginia wth so mch favour & Candor; & more especialy since I recd the particular obligation of the Letter I should have beene more speedy in my returne: But I begg both theirs and your pardon, it haveing beene extrordinary business has diverted me.   But let this assure both them, & you that I shall for the future be wanting in nothing, as far forth, as I am capable of Serveing them or you.   As for the Ingenious & Wonderfull experimts of the industrious Dr. Hooke,[2] in the account of wch you have mch hond & obliged me.   We wonder not here so mch at the melting of the Iron by the blast of a paire of Bellows, since it is very observable & common in the Iron forges, to see the mettle Run where the blast of Bellows comes immediately to the Mettle, when it is first come to a White heat, & the coles & fire are burnt & blown away absolutely & clearly from that part of the Mettle.   never the less it is very surprizeing, & new, to

[1] The original of this letter is in the Royal Society Archives, C 2.23/11–14, and was not published in *Phil. Trans*. It was read before the Society at the same time as Clayton's paper on the beasts of Virginia.   The Journal Book (VII, 241) noted on June 6 the reading of the latter article, remarking that it was concluded "with Some Remarks he had made on the Vast Elastick power of the Vapours of Water in the Experiments of Mr. Papin's Digesting Engine."

[2] Hooke is generally credited with having first applied the term "cell" to the basic units of plants.

heare of it done by a paire of Chamber bellows, & wt I have not had the leasure & conveniency to trie & a friend of mine, that has great concerne in Iron forges, goeing to trie it at one of the forges, could not procure a paire of Chamber bellows in all these parts, they haveing such fires as never to trouble them, or use any: but two men being sett to trie to heat Iron by hammering, could wth mch a doe bring it to a red heat; but all their force, & power, could not bring it to a white heat, wch is the welding heat. As to the aire being a common monstrum, & more specially its influences, & operations, upon Iron, are wonderfull, & might deserve a peculiar treatise, how it hardens, softens, alters, dissolves & luxates[3] wth Iron. I shall not trouble wth repetition of the several experiments that have been produced by the worthy members of the honorable Society but mention one, or two, that I think have not been before them of the luxation of Water wth Iron, & refer it to the great masters of Reasons, yourselfe I meane & the rest of members of the Society, whether it be not the Aire chiefly that is contained in the Water that produces that effect; or that rather as by some particular experiments. I have been inclined to think that Water it selfe is only Aire condensed, when the Spring of the Aire, is so close shut that by some particular means it cannot of its selfe open its selfe again and exert its elastic powr. for this is it of wch I have some notion, that the Spring of the Aire seemes to be governed by heat, & cold, the heat expanding & the cold shutting that Spring. That when the cold has so deepresd & shutt the Spring of the Aire to a certain degree, it can no more of itselfe exert its elastick power, but thereby ceases to be aire, & becomes water, till by the power of the fire, the same be opend again & as in the Cock of a pistol it pulls the tricker, & the Spring that way held fast is not at liberty again. I think a very considerable degree of heat

[3] To displace.

requisite for the unlocking these Springs; but when it is effected the springiness is a mighty force, however the most prodigious efforts of Water thus expanded or opend, even as strong as that of Gunpouder. Such as these. It is common for the forge men when they see a staring, gapeing Country-fellow, to take a little Water & sett it ready, & when He's gazeing about, & pretty nigh, to clap in a piece of Iron mettle of a White heat, & it will make as great a Crack, as any Musket, & surprize him much. But wt is most prodigious. It so happend, that once one of the Mil Dams of a forge burst on a Suddain, when there was a great many Tunns of Iron Oare melted in the furnace, & ready to be set forth; the flud of Water came Suddainly on the fire, & furnace, the Melted Oare & Water meeting together blew up the Furnance wth the most prodigious sort of Thunder crack & Shake to all the Country round about that can be imagined, Shot massy pieces of the building a considerable way, that the Shock of the blowing up Hackney Pouder Mills was not mch greater if so great: This I have from persons of great integrity, whereof the Royal Society has had no account, it being some years Since; I shall upon notice & their command get a particular Relation, & sende – . Some possibly will refer this to the Nitre of the Aire in the Water & the Sulphure of the mettle; possibly somthing of that nature may promote, but I have other notions thereof, tho I shall not contend as pro Aris et focis for my opins & slight conceptions of things, but submit myselfe to the mch acuter genius & judgment of you Gentlemen, but I do give you a brief account of an accident that happend. I had one of Mr. Papines new Digesters,[4] of his first invention; I was makeing some Experiments therein, & have-

---

[4] See his account of this same incident written to Robert Boyle in 1687 (pp. 11–14) and the one printed in *Phil. Trans.* in 1739, given here on pp. 140–43.

ing some Avocations made an extrordinary fire & left it: I suppose some of the Scrues gave way & the Irons that held the head on Slipt, at my returne I found the head had blown up the Chimbly, & hiting presently the ends of two bricks had cut them very smoothly; so that it was manifest it had gone wth a mighty force. It was this and another accident of the like nature made me contrive my Sort of New Digester wch I have formerly shown to the Royal Society, & to Mr. Papine himself just before his goeing as I remember to Madgeburg, wch is made of plates of Copper raised into a hollow cilinder by hamering & the edges laping over 2 Iron hopes made answerable to each other, through wch goe halfe a dozen Scrues more or less according to the biggness to scrue the head, & body together, & to keep it close: after wch maner I have invented a perpetual Balneum Marsi[5] that is one wherein the Water wasts not, wch I have used thus several years. I lived some years since in Huntingdon Shire where I had the happiness of Sr. Thomas Proby's acquaintance, he haveing heard of my new Digester desired to see it, & being one day to goe over to his house, I put a small one that would hold about a pint into my pocket. This was not made of raised Copper as aforesd, but had the bottom sawderd, it being designed only for the inward Cilinder, as in Mr. Papine's, but would serve well enough to show both the manner thereof & any common experimt. In this I inclosed a piece of the Marrow Bone of an Oxe in faire Water & heating it on the fire about nine minutes, when it was cooled that I could open it, the bone was very soft. Sr Thomas was mch pleased & surprized thereat, asking me in how short a time I could boile a bone soft, I told him I believed it possible to be done in 5 or 6 minutes time: but that the fire must be so quick and the inward pressure would be so great, that the

---

[5] A warm water bath. Clayton's contrivance must have been a type of double boiler.

Digester I thought would not be strong enough, being the bottom was only sauderd in & not raised as my other Digesters were. However Sr Thomas showing some desire to have it tried, we enclosed another bone in like maner as before, & put the end of the Digester betwixt the bars of the fire-Iron horizontally into the fire. In three minutes time by the Watch, I perceived the pressure was very violent. Sr Thomas was blowing the fire wth a paire of bellows to make the heat as great as we could contrive. I desired him to sitt further off, being forewarned by the aforesd accidents. he was just re-moveing the Chair, when it burst, & the Digester blew across the Roome, that was 7 or 8 yards long, hitt the leafe of an oval table & split the table board wch was of oake & an Inch thick all in pieces, & rebounded back again allmost to the fire. The explosion or Crack was like that of a musket, shooke the very house & was heard at a considerable distance. it blew out all the fire forth of the Range. Sr Thomas had his knee hurt so that it pufft up & sweld; he thought it was wth the rebounding blast of Water; for had it been wth one of the coles, or Cinders, or the like, it would have made a contusion or bruise, but there was not the least to be discerned, & it quickly settled wth being anointed wth Brandy, & a good Bandage. I imediatly looked for the Symptoms of Water I could discern any where, but there was not the least to be discovered, though we put in a full pint, so that it was all vanished into Aire and Vapor. Wt I conceive therefore of the Oare and Water makeing such a thunder clap, & blowing up the furnace & very foundations thereof, may be something of the like; for we see when Iron is upon melting, the parts that are Suddainly cooled are apt to forme themselves into little sort of Grenado shells,[6] as you instanced in that experiment of Dr. Hookes, & as is notorious

---

[6] From the French word for pomegranate. At one time this term was applied to any explosive shell fired from a gun.

in every Smiths forge: so that Water being first included in these Grenadoes & then immediately further heated & expanded into Aire, breakes the Grenadoes & thence the explosion: but this I submit to you, only this I shall add that by many experiments I find the pressure of Water or selfe of the Aire that lies latent & compresd in Water, is mch stronger than that of Aire alone when heated wth fire. But I begg pardon for this Discussion & shall only subjoyne in short, that if I truly set forth would be a mch longer Epistle. How mch I am,

Yr most Devoted humble Servant
J Clayton

Wakefield, May 22, 1694

You was pleasd to promise me most kindly the Transactions of the Royal S. next Vol. you are pleasd to honour me wth your G. Nature if you give but yourselfe the trouble to send them to Mdm Bradshaw's the Matron of the Charter house.[7] She will take care of them & they will be most kindly accepted by your most obliged

J C

[7] The Charterhouse "Hospital" for children and elderly men, located at that time on the site of a Carthusian monastery. It was the forerunner of the present-day public school of that name now located near Godalming. The Bradshaws were an old Lancashire family, but whether the matron was a member of it by marriage is not known.

XIII

"I HEREWTH SEND YOU A FOSSILE"
[*Third Letter to Waller*][1]

I herewth send you a Fossile just as it is taken out of the earth wthout any refineing. I take it to be an Alumen Scissile.[2] I desire to have your sentiments thereof & some of your friends advice that are best versed therein wt they judge it may be worth the hundred for I can procure considerable quantitys thereof   I take it to be a very fine sort of alum.

I have also a considerable parcel of the finest Sulphur-vive[3] I ever saw. I desire to know the best way of refineing it, the best way of Sublimeing the flowrs I ever saw was to make a little Roome about a yard broad two yards and a halfe long two yards tall the walls very smooth & therein sett an Iron Pott the mouth of the furnace haveing all its vents into another Roome; so fill the pot wth Sulphure & the flowers would Sublime & stick to the walls of that little roome, when the door was luted close up: & when the operation was done we swept together all the flowers & gatherd them.

But somwhere I have red of their melting it down wth Resin when they cast it into balls but this upon melting turns black

---

[1] The original of this letter is in the Archives of the Royal Society, C 2.24. A note at the bottom reads "Do to Mr Waller, accompanying some Alumen seissile, and describing methods of subliming Sulphur-vive into flowers." (see Plate IV, facing p. 65.)

[2] Apparently fossil alum which is noted for a tendency to split into layers or lamina.

[3] Natural or virgin sulphur.

the common cilinders of brimstone most certainly have Resin
in them, as I remember the acct is at full in Kircher[4] but I have
him not by me at present. I will send some of this Sulphur my
next, but have it not wth me at present & my friend is just for
takeing horse: therefore I must conclude wthout further cere-
mony than the full assurance that I am your most obliged
humble friend & Servant

J Clayton

June 20, 1694—Rich'd Waller, Esq. Secretary of the Royal
  Society.

[4] Father Athanasius Kircher (1602–80) , a scientist of some note.

XIV

CHINA VARNISH
By Mr John Clayton[1]

℞[2] a chopping[3] of spirit of Wine,[4] Gumme Lacquering Sanda-rac[5] ℥i:[6] put them all in a Madras glasse[7] very well stopt, & the drugs being very well pecked[8] sett in a B. M:[9] the space of three dayes, then strain it through a fine linning cloth and keept it very close stopt.

𝒩𝐵   The spirit of wine must be the highest rectified, it will be better in a bolbshead[10] sealed up hermetically.[11]   The reddest & clearest gummes are the best.

THE WAY TO LAY ON THE VARNISH

First warme wood by the fire, and lay on one covering of varnish with a big pensel.[12]   When you colour oake combine as

[1] From "A Copy of a Register Book of the Royal Society No. 1 being discourses, observations, & experiments registered" (B.M. 243 f. 150 [Article 28]). There is also a copy in the Archives of the Royal Society. It has not been established with certainty that the Reverend John Clayton wrote this note, but it was probably by him.

[2] Prescription symbol meaning "take."   [3] English wine quart.

[4] Alcohol.

[5] A brittle, faintly aromatic, translucent resin obtained from the sandarac tree, *Tetraclinis articulata,* of Morocco.   [6] One ounce.

[7] "Madras glasse" has not been identified; presumably it was made in Madras, India.

[8] Punctured or broken up.   [9] *Balneum Marsi,* a warm water bath.

[10] A flask (?).

[11] Alcohol of high concentration not only evaporates rapidly, but also takes up water from the air.

[12] A brush of hair or bristles used to lay on colors.

much varnish as colour and mingle them well together then Lay on four coverings of the mixt colour, & dry it at the fire whiles & you may tell [illeg.; perhaps, if dry] between every covering if you goe too neare the fire it will blister, then with your fingers put them down, then give it 4 coverings more after rub it over with sallad oyle & tripoli,[13] with a linnen cloth. Then lay on two coverings more of pure varnish, and rub it with sallad oyle & tripoli, lastly rub it with a fine linnen cloth the more you rub it the better.

TO MAKE THE BEST RED:

Take vermillion of Spain,[14] with a third part of Lac de Venise.[15]

[13] Soft deposits of silica, including diatomite. These are widely used today in various mild abrasives, as in many silver polishes.

[14] A bright-red pigment consisting of mercuric sulphide.

[15] Shellac, obtained from a scale insect, *Tachardia lacca*.

XV

PETITION OF THE REVEREND JOHN CLAYTON[1]

To his Grace the Duke
of Ormond Lord Lieutenant–
General and General Governour
of Ireland[2]
The humble petition of John Clayton –
Prebendary of Christ Church

May it please yr Grace

WHEREAS in the Case betwixt the Lord Arch Bishop of
Dublin[3] and the Dean and Chapter of Christ Church a petition
was presented by the Lord Bishop of Kildare Dean of Christ
Church[4] to her Majesty praying that her Majesty would be
gratiously pleasd to direct her Council and Advocates to de-
fend her Majestys Rights and priviledges   Whereupon her
Majesty was gratiously pleasd to refer the Same to your Grace
to Examin the allegations thereof and report your opinion
what is fitt to be done   And yr Grace referd the same to the
Attorney and Sollicitor General of Ireland who after many
days hearing of Council on both sides did draw up and sign a
Report directed to your Grace   But upon translation of the

---

[1] Printed from B.M. Add. MSS 21,132. Probably written in late 1705.
[2] Lieutenant-general and governor of Ireland.   [3] William King.
[4] William Moreton, Dean of Christ Church, 1677–1705, and Bishop of
Kildare, 1681–1705. For details of the controversy, see pp. l–liii.

Bishop of Kildare and Dean of Christ Church to the Bishopprick of Meath[5] the same Report is as yr petioner understands some way dropt tho it cost some hundreds of pounds to the prejudice of your petitioner who has an Appeal upon a branch of the said Cause whereby the whole Cause will come to be controverted and determined Now whereas the Stress of the Cause lies upon the Validity or Invalidity of her Majestys Charters and certain Branches of the Prerogative and Supremacy.

> Your petioner humbly prays your Grace to make the said Report to her Majesty and desire her to order a prohibition to be issued forth against the sd Lord Arch Bp of Dublin to stop his proceeding as was done in the Case of Dr. Kingston Minister of the Holy Trinity of Cork in Ireland one of the Queens Chappells other precidents of the like Nature I have found in the Tower of London one or two of wch I have presumed to transcribe the Lawyers being unacquainted wth these things as out of Common practice

> J. Clayton

[5] Sometime in 1705.

XVI

"SEVERALL OF THE PARISHIONERS
OF ST. MICHANS, ARE DISSATISFIED"
Letter to the Archbishop of Dublin[1]

To his Grace the Ld Arch Bishop of Dublin

Primate & Metropolitan of Ireland –

Whereas Severall of the Parishioners of St. Michans, are Dissatisfied wth mr. Needhams Preaching, and are Desirous to have a Lecturer to preach in the afternoon, & have sollicited me to Lett you have one, whom they & I will pay & support by contribution & being pleased wth the preaching of Revd. mr. Ambrose Upton, Master of Arts, who was formerly Curate here, they pitch upon him; Wherefore I humbly nominate & recommend the sd. mr. Upton to yr Grace, that if you approve thereof, you wd. please to Lisence him thereto, & being mr. Needham is only curate assistant, I Desire yr. Grace to Lay yr Commands on him only to read Prayers, that there may be noe disorder or bustle in the Church: I have Compassion on the man & therefore Dont desire, that any thing of his Personal Sallary shd. be abated or Deducted upon that acct.

I am   yr Graces
Most Dutifull & humble Servant
J. Clayton

Dublin Septr. 7th. 1725

[1] MSS Div. 2133. Trinity College, Dublin.

APPENDIX

ROBERT CLAYTON, BISHOP OF CORKE, TO THE EARL OF EGMONT[1]

London Dec. 23, 1740

My Lord

The kind reception which those few papers I have sent to your Lordsp. have met with both from your Lordsp. & the Gentlemen of the Royal Society encourages me to trouble you with the enclosed. And as some of the matters therein contained are of no small concernment to Mankind, if the gentlemen of the Royal Society approve thereof, I should not be averse to their being made publick. And as I apprehend it may contribute to encourage those who are enclined to pursue the hints therein given, if they were certified of the truth and genuineness of these papers, I do here in the most solemn manner take upon me to vouch for them; as far as concerns the sincerity and faithfullness of my copying them from the Original; which I found among my father's papers & in his own hand writing. As for the candour of the author & the truth of the matters of fact therein contained, I must leave that to the world to judge of, but in my opinion they speak sufficiently in

---

[1] Taken from the manuscript in Papers Relating to the Royal Society, B.M., Birch Collection, 4437, f. 50. The outside of the letter bears the following notation: Jan. 22, 1740 Entd. L. B. Robt. Bp. of Corke to Earl of Egmont with papers of the Revd. Jo. Clayton DD."

their own vindication, & do not stand in need of any other
Justification.

> I am My Lord
> Your Lordsps
> Most obedient
> Humble Servant
> Robt Corke

To the Rt Honble
Earl of Egmont

V. AN EXPERIMENT CONCERNING THE *SPIRIT OF COALS* INTER ALIA IN A LETTER TO THE HONBLE *MR. BOYLE* BY YE LATE REVD JO CLAYTON DD COMMUNICATED BY THE RIGHT REVD FATHER IN GOD ROBERT LORD BISHOP OF CORKE TO THE RIGHT HONBLE EARL OF EGMONT F. R. S.[2]

Having seen a ditch within two miles of Wigan in Lancashire wherein the water would seemingly burn like Brandy,
the flame of which was so fierce that several strangers have
boiled Eggs over it.   The people thereabouts indeed affirm
that about 30 years ago it would have boiled a piece of beef, &
that whereas much rain formerly made it burn much fiercer
now after rain it would scarce burn at all.   It was after a long
continued season of rain that I came to see the place & make

[2] Taken from the manuscript in Papers Relating to the Royal Society,
B.M., Birch Collection, 4437, f. 52. This experiment appeared, with a few
changes in spelling, in *Phil. Trans.*, XLI (1739) , 59–61.

some Experiments & found accordingly that a lighted paper though it were waved all over the ditch the water would not take fire. I then hired a person to make a dam in the ditch, & fling out the water in order to try whether the stream which arose from the ditch would then take fire, but found it would not. I still however pursued my Experiment & made him dig deeper & when he had dugg about the depth of half a yard we found a shelly coal, & the candle being then putt down into the hole the air catched fire & continued burning.

I observed that there had formerly been coal pits in the same close of ground & I then gott some coal from one of the pits nearest thereunto which I distilled in a Retort in an open fire. At first there came over only *fleghm,* afterwards a black *oyle,* & then likewise a *Spirit* arose which I could no ways condense but it forced my lute or broke my glasses. Once when it had forced my lute coming close thereto in order to try to repair it, I observed that the Spirit which issued out caught fire at the flame of the candle & continued burning with violence as it issued out, in a stream; which I blew out, & light again, alternately for several times. I then had a mind to try if I could save any of this spirit, in order to which I took a turbinated Receiver & putting a candle to the pipe of the Receiver whilst the spirit arose I observed that it catched flame & continued burning At the end of the pipe though you could not discern what fed the flame I then blew it out & light it again several times, after which I fixed a bladder squeezed & void of air to the pipe of the Receiver. The oyle & fleghm descended into the Receiver but the spirit still ascending blew up the bladder. I then filled a good many bladders therewith, & might have filled an inconceivable number more for the spirit continued to rise for several hours & filled the bladders almost as fast as a man could have blown them with his mouth, & yet the quantity of coals I distilled were inconsiderable.

I kept this spirit in the bladder a considerable time, & endeavoured several ways to condense it, but in vain. And when I had a mind to divert strangers or friends I have frequently taken one of these bladders & pricking a hole therein with a pin & compressing gently the bladder near the flame of a candle till it once took fire it would then continue flaming till all the spirit was compressed out of the bladder which was the more surprising because no one could discern any difference in the appearance between these bladders, & those which are filled with common air.

But then I found that this Spirit must be kept in good thick bladders, as in those of an Ox or the like, for if I filled calves bladders therewith it would loose its inflammability in 24 hours, though the bladder became not relax at all.

II. AN EXPERIMENT TO PROVE THAT WATER WHEN AGITATED BY FIRE IS INFINITELY MORE ELASTICK THAN AIR IN THE SAME CIRCUMSTANCES[3]

Sir Thos Proby having heard of a new Digester which I contrived had a desire to see it & some experiments made therein. I had a small one which I designed only for an inward cylinder this I could easily put in my pocket where-

[3] Taken from the manuscript in Papers Relating to the Royal Society, B.M., Birch Collection, 4437, f. 102. Added in a different handwriting is the following note: "by the late Revd. John Clayton Dean of Kildare in Ireland Communicated by the same Hand as ye preceding – ". The experiment appeared in *Phil. Trans.*, XLI (1739), 162–66.

fore going to pay him a visit at Elton in Huntingdonshire I took it along with me & having softened a bone therein in a very short space he was desirous to know the shortest time it was possible to soften a bone in. I told him I thought I could soften the marrow bone of an Ox in a very few minutes, but that that vessel was very weak & I fear'd would not endure the pressure of so violent a heat, yet seeming desirous to have the experiment tried I said I was ready to venture my vessel, then having fixed all things right & included about a pint of water & I believe about ʒii [two ounces] of a Marrow bone, we placed the vessel Horizontally betwixt the bars of the Iron Grate into the fire about halfway, & in 3 minutes time I found it raised to a great heat whereupon I had a mind to have taken it out of the fire least it should burst telling Sir Thos of the danger that I apprehended. For I remember'd that the screws of a digester made after Mr. Papine's method giving way the head flew one way & the screws & Irons another with such violence that the head having hitt against a brick cutt a piece cleverly out of it, which was one reason & motive to my contriving a Digester this way that the screws cannot possibly start, but that the vessel would sooner break in any other part. But in this <I added> I thought the bottom would first burst it being only soudred in. Scarce had I done speaking & Sr Thos thereupon moved his chair to avoid danger but seeing the heat become more raging, I step'd to the side table for the Iron wherewith I managed the digester, in order to take it out of the fire, when on a suddain it burst as if a musket had gone off, a maid that was gone a milking heard it at a considerable distance, the servants said it shook the House; as I had foretold the bottom of the vessel that was in the fire gave way, the blast of the expanded water blew all of the coals out of the fire all over the Room for the back of the fire range was made just like an oven so that circulating therein it brought forth all the coals at the mouth thereof. All the vessel together flew in a direct line cross the room and hitting the leaf of a table made of an inch oak plank broke it all in pieces & rebounded half way of the room back again. What surprized me in this event was that the noise it made at its bursting was by no means like the successive evaporating of an Eolipipe, but like the firing off of Gunpowder. Nor could I perceive any where in the room the least sign of water though I looked carefully for it, & as I said before I had put a pint into the digester, save only that the fire was quite extinguished, and every coal belonging to it was black in an instant.

But to confirm the Elasticity of Water or to show at least that there is a much stronger Elastick force in Water & air when Joyntly included in a vessel than when air alone is enclosed therein I made the following Experiment. I took two ℥vi [six-ounce] vials into the one I put about ℥v [five ounces] ounces of water or better and so corked it as well as I possibly could, the other I corked in the same manner, without putting anything into it. I inclosed them both in my new Digester, four fifths being filled with water when the heat was raised to about 5 seconds, I heard a considerable explosion & a jingling of glass within the vessel & shortly after another explosion but not so loud as the former, whence I concluded that both of the vials were broken I then lett the Digester cool leisurely & the next day I opened it, both the corks were swimming on the top of the water, but only one of the vials was broken, viz that one into which I had not put any water. At first indeed I concluded that the pressure or dilation of the air in the empty vial being stronger than the ambient pressure forced forth the cork where upon the water rushing in with violence might break the vial, & therefore that this was the cause also of the loudness of the explosion, whereas the other being mostly filled with water, there being but a small quantity of air therein just enough to force out the corke the vial was not broken, but was preserved by the force of the water enclosed therein. But I have had reason since to change my opinion for having had very strong vials made on purpose to make some peculiar experiments therewith, I took one of them & having filled it about quarter full with water & corked it very well, I sett it in a square iron frame with a screw to screw down the cork & keep it from flying forth. I then put it into a Digester four fifths filled with water which being heated to a due height, when I opened it I found the cork forced into the bottle. Hence it manifestly appears that the pressure in the digester wherein was proportionately more water & less air was stronger than the pressure within the vial wherein was proportionately more air & less water. Then I reasoned thus also of the 2 former vials. That the air in the vial wherein was no water included making not a proportionate resistance to the ambient pressure in the Digester wherein was a considerable quantity of water the Cork was forced inward with such violence that it together with the water dashed the vial in pieces; But that in the other vial wherein there were 5/6ths of water the inward pressure in the vial being greater than the ambient pressure in the Digester, wherein were but 4/5ths of water, the cork was thereby forced outward, and that the small difference between the proportional quantity of water & air in the vial & in the Digester being only as 4/5ths to 5/6ths was the reason not only why the bottle was not broken, but also of the faintness of the explosion.

VI. EXPERIMENT CONCERNING
THE NITROUS PARTICLES IN THE AIR
BY THE SAME HAND[4]

I took a small gally-pot, such as the apothecarys in the North of England make use of where I was when I made this experiment, & ground the top of it very smooth & true & adapted thereto a cover of blew slate which I had likewise ground with much care. Into this gally-pot I put equall quantitys of Nitre & flower of Sulphur about an ℥i [one ounce] of each   I then fixed on the cover putting it into a new digester, but the height which I raised the heat to & how long I continued it I do not exactly remember; but believe it was 3 or 4 seconds. When I opened it the day following I perceived something had transpired betwixt the top of the gally-pot & the cover, the top edges of the gally-pot where the glazing was ground off being discoloured, though the nitre & sulphur were very little diminished as to their weight, only they were melted into one lump, which I took out of the gally-pot.

And having left the empty gally-pot upon a shelf, upon looking at it the next day I found long hoary hairs very bright & brittle all around the ground edges of the pott very specious to behold. After I had admired them a while I gathered them, & tasted them, & found them to be pure nitre. I then left the pott upon the shelf again & in 3 or 4 days still finding there were shoots made as large & specious as at the first I gathered them a 2d & 3d time. So that I suppose the pot would have

---

[4] Taken from the manuscript in Papers Relating to the Royal Society, B.M., Birch Collection, 4437, f. 53. The experiment appeared in *Phil. Trans.*, XLI (1739), 62–63.

continued to have that fresh nitre much longer, if I had not had urgent use for it to make other experiments in. However it is to be observed that I had already gathered more nitre than I putt into the Pot at first, though as I said before for what I could perceive I had taken all or near all the nitre that I first put in together with the sulphur out of the pot in Lump. Hence we may have some conception of the nature of mineral earths & how they grow & increase when once impregnated with the seeds of a mineral. This likewise is a proof of the quantity of nitrous particles with which the air abounds since the large quantity of nitre which I collected out of the pott when left empty upon the shelf could be supplied by the air only.

NOTE BY BISHOP CLAYTON[5]

NB

These 3 Experiments are all that I could save entire out of a great number which were sent to the Honble. Mr. Boyle in answer to a letter from him to Mr. John Clayton containing 17 Quaeres.

Robt Corke

[5] This note was added to the end of the experiment on nitrous particles.

OBSERVATIONS OF THE COMPARATIVE, INTENSIVE OR SPECIFIC GRAVITIES OF VARIOUS BODIES MADE BY MR. J. C.[1]

Pump-water	1000	Succinum pellucidem[8]	1065
Cork	237	Succinum pingue[9]	1087
Sassafras Wood	482	Jet	1238
Juniper Wood (dry)	556	The top part of a	
Plum-tree (dry)	663	Rhinoceros horn	1242
Mastic[2]	849	The top part of an Ox-	
Santulum Citrinum[3]	809	horn	1840
Santulum album[4]	1041	The (Blade) of an Ox	1656
Santulum rubrum[5]	1128	An human Calculus[10]	1240
Ebony		Another Calculus Hu-	
Lignum Rhodium[6]	1125	manus	1433
Lignum Asphaltum[7]	1179	Another Calculus hu-	
Aloes	1177	manus	1664

[1] Reprinted from *Phil. Trans.*, XVII (1693), 694–95. Boyle had just published a book on this subject.

[2] Resin from the European tree *Pistacia lentiscus* L. used in varnishes and as an astringent.

[3] An unidentified member of the Santalaceae, or sandalwood family, which includes mainly herbs and shrubs, with a few trees.

[4] An Indo-Malayan parasitic tree, *Santalum album* L.

[5] Probably *Lingoum santalinum*, a tree belonging to the pea family and growing in the East Indies.

[6] The fragrant Rhodium wood, either from the roots or stem of *Convolvulus scoparius* or *C. virgatus*, shrubs of the island of Teneriffe.

[7] Asphalt is sometimes a residue from lignite tar, so perhaps this is the explanation for this term. Probably native asphalt is meant.

[8] Clear amber?

[9] Pingue means "fat" or "fatty"; possibly it refers here to cloudy amber.

[10] A concretion formed in the body, such as a kidney stone.

Brimstone, such as commonly sold[11]	1811	A red Paste Lapis Nephriticus[18]	2894
Borax	1720	Lapis Amiantus from Wales[19]	2931
A spotted factitious Marble	1822	Lapis Lazuli	3054
A Galley-Pot	1928	An Hone[20]	3288
Oyster shell	2092	Sardachates[21]	3598
Murex-shell[12]	2590	A Granat	3978
Lapis manati[13]	2270	A Golden Marcasite	4589
Silenitis[14]	2322	A blew Slate with shining Particles	3500
Wood petrified in Lough-Neagh	2341	A mineral stone, yielding 1 part in 160 Metal	2640
Onyx stone	2510	The Metal thence extracted	8500
Turcois-stone	2508	The (reputed) Silver Ore of Wales	7464
English Agat	2512	The Metal thence extracted	11087
Grammatis lapis[15]	2515	Bismuth	9859
A Cornelian	2568	Spetter[22]	7065
Corallachates[16]	2605	Spetter Soder	8362
Talc	2657	Iron of a Key	7643
Coral	2680	Steel	7852
Hyacinth (Spurious)	2631	Cast Brass	8100
Jasper (Spurious)	2666	Wrought Brass	8280
A pellucid Pebble	2641		
Rock Crystal	2659		
Crystallum Disdea elasticum[17]	2704		

[11] Sulphur.   [12] A shellfish of the genus *Murex* with a rough shell.

[13] Manatis or sea cows are tropical aquatic animals of the genus *Trichechus* of the order Sirenia. Clayton may refer to a concretion found in one of them.

[14] Unidentified.   [15] Unidentified.   [16] A type of coral?

[17] A piece of comparatively translucent rubber?

[18] An artificial jade, worn sometimes as a kidney cure.

[19] Amianthus, a form of asbestos.   [20] A fine whetstone.

[21] Probably sard, an orange-red type of chalcedony from Sardinia.

[22] Unidentified.

Hammered Brass	8349	A *Mentz* Gold Ducat	18261
A false Guinea	9075	A Gold Coin of	
A true Guinea	18888	*Alexanders*	18893
Sterling Silver	10535	A Gold Medal of	
A brass Half-Crown	9468	*Q. Mary*	19100
Electrum, a British		A Gold Medal of	
Coin	12071	*Q. Elizabeth*	19125
A Gold Coin of		A Medal esteem'd to be	
Barbary	17548	near fine Gold	19636
A Gold Medal from			
Morocco	18420		

BIBLIOGRAPHY

Abernethy, T. P. *Three Virginia Frontiers*. Baton Rouge, La., 1940.

Allen, E. G. "The History of American Ornithology before Audubon," *Transactions of the American Philosophical Society*, XLI, Part 3 (1951), 459–61.

Alvord, C. W., and Lee Bidgood (eds.). *The First Explorations of the Trans-Allegheny Region by the Virginians, 1650–1674*. Cleveland, 1912.

Anderson, J. S. M. *The History of the Church of England in the Colonies*. 2 vols. London, 1856.

Bailey, Worth. "Lime Preparation at Jamestown in the Seventeenth Century," *William and Mary Quarterly*, ser. 2, XVIII (1938), 1–12.

Baines, Edward. *The History of the County Palatine and Duchy of Lancaster*. Ed. James Croston. 5 vols. London, 1893.

Baines, Thomas. *History of the Commerce and Town of Liverpool*. London, 1852.

Berkeley, Edmund and D. S. *John Clayton, Pioneer of American Botany*. Chapel Hill, N.C., 1963.

Birch, Thomas. *History of the Royal Society of London*. 4 vols. London, 1727.

Blanton, W. B. *Medicine in Virginia in the Seventeenth Century*. Richmond, 1930.

Boas, Marie. *Robert Boyle and Seventeenth-Century Chemistry*. Cambridge, 1958.

Boyle, Robert. *The Philosophical Works of the Honourable Robert Boyle Esq*. Ed. Peter Shaw. 3 vols. London, 1725.

Boyle, Robert. *The Works of the Honourable Robert Boyle.* Ed. Thomas Birch. 6 vols. London, 1772.

Britten, James, and G. S. Boulger. *British and Irish Botanists.* London, 1931.

Brodrick, G. C. *Memorials of Merton College.* Oxford, 1885.

Brooks, E. St. J. *Sir Hans Sloane.* London, 1954.

Brooks, J. E. *The Mighty Leaf.* Boston, 1952.

Browne, C. A. "Reverend Dr. John Clayton and His Early Map of Jamestown, Virginia," *William and Mary Quarterly,* ser. 2, XIX (1939) , 1–7.

Bruce, P. A. *Institutional History of Virginia in the Seventeenth Century.* 2 vols. New York, 1910.

Bryant, H. C. "The First Recorded Lists of Birds in the United States," *Auk,* LI (1934) , 451–53.

Brydon, G. MacL. "Historic Parishes, I. James City Parish in Virginia," *Historical Magazine of the Protestant Episcopal Church,* IX (1942) , 69.

———. *Virginia's Mother Church.* 2 vols. Richmond, 1947–52.

Burnaby, Andrew. *Travels through the Middle Settlements in North-America in the years 1759 and 1760.* London, 1775; reprinted, Ithaca, N.Y., 1960.

Burtchaell, G. D., and T. U. Sadleir. *Alumni Dublinenses.* Dublin, 1936.

Bushnell, D. I. "Virginia from Early Records," *American Anthropologist,* IX (1907) , 31–56.

Byrd, William. "Letters of William Byrd, First," ed. W. G. Stanard, *Virginia Magazine of History and Biography,* XXIV (1916) , 225–236 and 350–60.

Cabell, N. F. *Early History of Agriculture in Virginia.* Washington, [18—].

Cameron, C. A. *History of the Royal College of Surgeons in Ireland.* Dublin, 1916.

Carpenter, E. F. *The Protestant Bishop.* London, 1956.

Chiang Yee. *The Silent Traveller in Dublin.* New York, 1953.

Cooke, J. E. *Virginia, A History of the People.* Boston, 1892.

Cork and Orrery, Emily, Countess of (ed.). *The Orrery Papers.* 2 vols. London, 1903.

Crone, J. S. *A Concise Dictionary of Irish Biography.* London, 1928.

Dictionary of National Biography. Ed. Leslie Stephen and Sidney Lee. London, 1917.

Donnan, Elizabeth. "Eighteenth Century English Merchants: Micajah Perry," *Journal of Economic and Business History,* IV (November 1931), 70–98.

Dugdale, William. *The Visitation of . . . Lancashire, . . . 1664–5, by Sir William Dugdale.* Ed. F. R. Raines. (Chetham Society, *Remains Historical & Literary . . . ,* Vol. LXXXIV.) Manchester, 1872.

Durand de Dauphiné. *A Huguenot Exile in Virginia.* Ed. Gilbert Chinard. New York, 1934.

Evelyn, John. *Memoirs Illustrative of the Life and Writings of John Evelyn, Esq.* F.R.S. Ed. William Bray. 2 vols. London, 1818.

Farrer, William, and John Brownbill (eds.). *Victoria History of Lancashire.* 8 vols. London, 1907–14.

Fenwick, G. L. *A History of the Ancient City of Chester.* Chester, Eng., 1896.

Fernow, Berthold. *Ohio Valley in Colonial Days.* Albany, 1890.

Fisher, M. S. *Robert Boyle, Devout Naturalist, A Study in Science and Religion in the Seventeenth Century.* Philadelphia, 1945.

Fishwick, Henry. *History of Lancashire.* London, 1894.

Fletcher, J. S. *A Picturesque History of Yorkshire.* 3 vols. London, 1900.

Forman, H. C. *Jamestown and St. Mary's.* Baltimore, 1938.

Foster, John. *Alumni Oxonienses, 1500–1714.* London, 1891.

Ganter, H. L. "Some Notes on the Charity of the Honourable Robert Boyle, Esq., of the City of London, Deceased," *William and Mary Quarterly,* ser. 2, XV (1935), 1–39.

Garner, W. W. *The Production of Tobacco.* Philadelphia, 1951.

Gastrell, Francis. *Notitia Cestriensis; or, Historic Notices of the Diocése of Chester.* Ed. F. R. Raines. (Chetham Society, *Remains, Historical & Literary* . . . , Vols. VIII, XIX, XXI, XXII.) Manchester, 1845–50.

Glover, Thomas. "An Account of Virginia," *Philosophical Transactions,* XI (1676), 623–36.

Goodwin, E. L. *The Colonial Church in Virginia.* London, 1927.

Granville, Mary. *The Autobiographies and Correspondence of Mary Granville, Mrs. Delaney.* Ed. the Rt. Hon. Lady Llanover. 3 vols. London, 1861.

Great Britain. *State Papers, Domestic, 1697.* Ed. W. J. Hardy. London, 1927.

——. Historical Manuscripts Commission. *Calendar of the Manuscripts of the Marquess of Ormonde, K.P., Preserved at Kilkenny Castle.* New ser. 8 vols. London, 1902–20.

Griffin, G. G. *A Guide to Manuscripts relating to American History in British Depositories Reproduced for the Division of Manuscripts of the Library of Congress.* Washington, 1946.

Gunther, R. T. *Early Science in Oxford.* 14 vols. Oxford, 1920–45.

Hartley, Harold (ed.). *The Royal Society, Its Origins and Founders.* London, 1960.

Hatch, C. E., Jr., and T. G. Gregory. "The First American Blast Furnace, 1619–1622," *Virginia Magazine of History and Biography,* LXX (1962), 259–96.

Hawks, F. L. *Rise and Progress of the Protestant Episcopal Church in Virginia.* 2 vols. New York, 1836.

Hoare, R. C. *Journal of a Tour in Ireland.* London, 1807.

Hoffman, B. C. "John Clayton's 1687 Account of the Medicinal Practices of the Virginia Indians," *Ethnohistory,* XI (Winter 1964), 1–40.

Houghton, John. *A Collection of Letters for the Improvement of Husbandry and Trade.* Ed. Richard Bradley. 3 vols. London, 1727.

Jefferson, Thomas. *Thomas Jefferson's Garden Book.* Ed. E. M. Betts. Philadelphia, 1944.

Johnston, T. J., J. L. Robinson, and R. W. Jackson. *A History of the Church of Ireland.* Dublin, 1953.

King, C. S. (ed.). *A Great Archbishop of Dublin, William King, D.D., 1650–1729.* London, 1906.

Layton, W. T. *The Discoverer of Gas Lighting, Notes on the Life and Work of the Reverend John Clayton D.D., 1657–1725.* London, 1926.

Lecky, W. E. H. *A History of Ireland in the Eighteenth Century.* 15 vols. London, 1912.

McAtee, W. L. "North American Bird Records in the 'Philosophical Transactions': 1665–1800," *Journal of the Society for Bibliography of Natural History,* III (December 1953), 46–60.

McCary, B. C. *Indians in Seventeenth-Century Virginia.* Williamsburg, Va., 1957.

Maxwell, Constantia. *Country and Town in Ireland under the Georges.* London, 1940.

——. *Dublin under the Georges, 1714–1830.* London, 1936.

——. *A History of Trinity College, Dublin 1591–1892.* Dublin, 1946.

Meade, William. *Old Churches, Ministers, and Families of Virginia.* 2 vols. Philadelphia, 1861.

Meigs, Guy. *The Present State of Great Britain and Ireland.* London, 1718.

Morton, R. L. *Colonial Virginia.* 2 vols. Chapel Hill, N.C., 1960.

Motherby, G. *A New Medical Dictionary.* 4th ed. London, 1795.

Moulin, Allen. "An Account of an Experiment of the Injection of Mercury into the Blood . . . Experiment at Mr. Boyle's," *Philosophical Transactions,* XV (1690), 486.

——. "Anatomical Observations in the heads of Fowel made at several times," *Philosophical Transactions,* XVII (1693), 711–16.

Moulin, Allen. "Some Experiments on a Black Shining Sand brought from Virginia, suppos'd to contain Iron," *Philosophical Transactions,* XVII (1692/3), 624–26.

Muir, Ramsay. *A History of Liverpool.* London, 1907.

Murray, J. J. "A Brief History of Virginia Ornithology," *Raven,* IV (March 1933), 2–11.

New York. *Documents Relative to the Colonial History of the State of New York.* Ed. E. B. O'Callaghan and B. Fernow. 15 vols. Albany, 1856–87.

Nichols, John. *Literary Anecdotes of the Eighteenth Century.* 9 vols. London, 1812–16.

Noel, Gerard. *Members of Parliament.* London, 1878.

Notes and Queries, ser. 10, Vol. XI (1909).

O'Brien, R. B. (ed.). *Two Centuries of Irish History, 1691–1870.* London, 1907.

Ormerod, George. *The History of the County Palatine and City of Chester.* Ed. Thomas Helsby. 3 vols. London, 1882.

Page, William (ed.). *The Victoria History of York.* 3 vols. London, 1913.

Page, William, Granville Proby, and S. I. Ladds (eds.). *The Victoria History of the County of Huntingdon.* 3 vols. Waterloo, 1930–36.

Pargellis, Stanley. "An Account of the Indians in Virginia," *William and Mary Quarterly,* ser. 3, XVI (1959), 228–43.

Perry, W. S. *Historical Collections Relating to the American Colonial Church.* 2 vols. Hartford, 1870.

––––. *The History of the American Episcopal Church.* 2 vols. Boston, 1885.

Plowden, Francis. *An Historical Review of the State of Ireland.* Philadelphia, 1805–6.

Redding, Cyrus. *An Illustrated Itinerary of the County of Lancaster.* London, 1842.

Reid, S. J. *John and Sarah, Duke and Duchess of Marlborough, 1660–1744.* London, 1914.

Robert, J. C. *The Story of Tobacco in America.* New York, 1949.

Royal Society of London. *The Record of the Royal Society of London.* 4th ed. London, 1940.

Salter, H. E., and M. D. Lobel (eds.). *The Victoria History of Oxford.* 3 vols. London, 1954.

Schorger, A. W. *The Passenger Pigeon.* Madison, Wis., 1955.

Semmes, Raphael. *Captains and Mariners of Early Maryland.* Baltimore, 1937.

Smith, J. F., Gordon Hemm, and A. E. Shennan. *Liverpool.* Liverpool, Eng., 1948.

Stevens, O. A. "The First Description of North American Birds," *Wilson Bulletin,* XLVIII (1936), 203–15.

Taylor, Silas. "Of a Way of Killing Rattle-Snakes," *Philosophical Transactions,* I (1665), 43.

Taylor, W. B. S. *History of the University of Dublin.* London, 1845.

Tilley, N. M. *The Bright-Tobacco Industry, 1860–1929.* Chapel Hill, N.C., 1948.

Tyler, L. G. "Virginia's Contribution to Science," *William and Mary Quarterly,* ser. 1, XIV (1916), 218–19.

Virginia. *Executive Journals of the Council of Colonial Virginia.* Ed. H. R. McIlwaine. Richmond, 1925.

——. *Journals of the House of Burgesses of Virginia, 1659/60– 1693.* Ed. H. R. McIlwaine. Richmond, 1914.

Ware, James. *The Whole Works of Sir James Ware concerning Ireland.* Ed. Walter Harris. Dublin, 1739–46.

Watson, William. "An Account of the Bishop of London's Garden at Fulham," *Philosophical Transactions,* XLVII (1751), 241– 47.

Weld, C. R. *History of the Royal Society.* 2 vols. London, 1848.

Wertenbaker, T. J. *The First Americans, 1607–1690.* Vol. II. New York, 1927.

White, G. W. "Early American Geology," *Scientific Monthly,* LXXVI (1953), 134–41.

Wilberforce, Samuel. *A History of the Protestant Episcopal Church in America.* New York, 1849.

Wolf, F. A. *Tobacco Diseases and Decays.* Durham, 1957.

Wood, Anthony à. *The Life and Times of Anthony Wood, Antiquary of Oxford, 1632–1695*. Ed. Andrew Clark. Oxford, 1892.

Yonge, S. H. "The Site of Old 'James Towne' 1607–1698," *Virginia Magazine of History and Biography*, XII (1904), 125–27.

Zirkle, Conway. "John Clayton and Our Colonial Botany," *Virginia Magazine of History and Biography*, LXVII (1959), 284–94.

INDEX

THE REVEREND JOHN CLAYTON
A Parson with a Scientific Mind

was composed, printed, and bound by
Kingsport Press, Inc., Kingsport, Tennessee.
The paper is Standard's Permalife
and the type is Baskerville with
Bulmer initials.
Design is by Edward Foss.